mexican folktales from the Borderland

From the

PUBLICATIONS OF THE TEXAS FOLKLORE SOCIETY

mexican folktales from the borderland

RILEY AIKEN

FOREWORD BY FRANCIS EDWARD ABERNETHY

DRAWINGS BY DENNIS ZAMORA

SOUTHERN METHODIST UNIVERSITY PRESS • DALLAS

Library of Congress Cataloging in Publication Data
Main entry under title:

Mexican folktales from the borderland.

"From the Publications of the Texas Folklore Society."
1. Tales, Mexican.   2. Indians of Mexico—Legends.
I. Aiken, Riley.   II. Texas Folklore Society.
GR115.M46   398.2'0972   79-25531
ISBN 0-87074-175-6

To my wife, Beulah

Contents

Foreword

I WALKED from above Solola to Panajachel on Lake Atitlán one cool, clean June morning, and my spirit soared to be in such a place. I watched a brown hawk drop from a pine tree and sail across the big valley, moving only his head as he hunted the green world below him. The time and place did not exist in relation to any other. The ends of the earth were just beyond the volcanoes across the big lake and behind the mountains that rose sharply beside the road and on the other side of the broad valley.

About halfway down the mountain road I stopped at a roadside stand that was draped with bright ponchos and shirts and dresses for sale to tourists. Nearby was a small covered stand where two children, a boy and a girl eight or nine years old, sold bottled drinks, Chiclets, and homemade candy. They joined their customers and sat in the shade on concrete benches and looked down on the most beautiful of all lakes. The center of the group was an old man who had stopped to rest from his load of firewood. He was ancient and grizzled and had four teeth spaced randomly. And he was a story-teller.

I don't think I could have understood him had I been proficient in Spanish, and his words were wet and strained through a moustache that hung far over his top lip. But I didn't have to understand all to know that here was a man who could tell a tale. What the whole of the story was I never made out, but it took place (I think) on a dark night in or around San Pedro, and it had ghosts and *fantasmas* and a *borrachón* as characters. Whatever the details of the story were, the telling of it was what was impressive. The old man spoke with a quiet but rapid intensity with no periods and few commas, making small but very descriptive gestures with his shoulders and his hands, one of which had only three fingers and the nub of a thumb. His eyes widened in fright to illustrate the terror of the story and then narrowed under eyebrows that repeated the overhang of his moustache. He sucked air through his gums and he made "ay-e-e-e" sounds, and the two child-merchants would get smaller in their seats, and the young man who sat beside him would thoughtfully turn over the machete that lay sheathed in his lap. No one, neither the young man, the children, nor I, took our attention from him during the four or five minutes—or hour or seconds—of the tale and when he was done he sat back, looked very thoughtful for a while, and then smiled and became himself again and asked us if we liked the story. At least, I think that is what he asked. I told him I liked it very much and he kept smiling, so I decided that I was communicating in Spanish. The little boy opened a box of Chiclets and the girl went over and leaned on his knee to see if he was the same man who had sat there before the story began. He soon arose and with cheery valedictions to all slipped on the head-band that supported his load of firewood, and he and the young man walked up the steep highway that led to Solola.

He told a tale. With his hands and eyes and gray hanging eye-brows and moustache he acted a story before an audience. With four teeth and a gray-looking tongue he made a series of happen-ings into a momentary reality more vivid than the gravel under our feet or the bright sun that shone above us. He was an artist.

Norteamericanos, for the most part, have lost the art of story-telling. It is a curse of literacy. We read our stories, or hear them on the radio or see them at movies or on TV. Sometimes we tell old tales to our children or make up stories, but usually we read the bedtime tale from a Little Golden Book. The one still-thriving oral tradition in gringo literature is the dirty joke, and that type of story is still a told story because that is the only way it can be circulated, not being accepted in proper literary circles.

I don't know whether my raisin' was normal or abnormal, but I don't remember many real folktales that came down to me through my family's oral traditions. My grandfather was a good storyteller and joke teller, but he passed on none of the folktales that were at one time a part of the Anglo-Saxon tradition. He did tell me the first jokes I ever heard. I think it was for want of a better audience, and because of the fact that I was always at his heels. He introduced me to the classic about the greenhorn who comes into the bar and seeing the sign on the wall very knowledgeably orders a glass of billiards. He told a long joke about an Irishman in West Texas who returned to the Old Sod and told incredulous listeners about the land where the wind pumped the water and the cows chopped the wood (he cooked over cow chips), and where the bugs played marbles and cow patties got up on their legs and walked (tumble-bugs and terrapins). When Uncle Sam visited the ranch we would sit on the steps after supper and he and Granddad would tell stories about their lives and adventures in Arkansas and Old Greer County. Uncle Sam, who had been a Baptist preacher, told stories from the Bible, which I had already heard. Every once in a while he told a few real tales, fictional stories with characters who got involved in conflicts that they finally overcame, but that was rare.

People have probably been telling tales since speech began, telling visions and thoughts that could be or that they hoped could be, shaping fragments of chaotic experiences into an orderly, comprehensible pattern. The telling of stories in the form of myths and legends and tales may be necessary to survival. Perhaps without the order that art, literary or otherwise, imposes on life, man's mind would spin off out of orbit. Man, like all other animals, requires order in his life, and because he cannot always find it he creates it in another literary life.

Riley Aiken's Mexican *cuentos* are another literary life. They are tales of wonder, adventure, and humor that had for their ancestry the folklore of the Old World and the New. Stories that had circulated in Europe for hundreds of years are here set in a Mexican village or *jacal* and cast with characters who still feel their Indian heritage. They are a blending of three cultural traditions.

Riley is an old-time Paisano in the Texas Folklore Society, and the stories in *Mexican Folktales from the Borderland* come from his contributions to the Society's publications from 1935 to 1964. They record a span of collecting and recording that covered more than thirty years. Riley was born on the Texas-Mexican border and lived on a ranch called Los Alamos Cesaria. He grew up in the setting of his stories and remembers them from his early childhood. His academic interest in collecting the stories began in 1929, and during his stay at the University of Texas he took them to J. Frank Dobie,

then editor of the Texas Folklore Society publications. Dobie liked
them and featured them in the 1935 Society publication, *Puro Mexicano*. Riley continued his collecting and publishing and worked
among Mexicans on both sides of the Rio Grande.

Riley has a distinct feel for the character and language of the
Mexican-Indian rural borderland culture, and he has the linguistic
capacity and sensitivity to communicate this feeling. He knows the
sound and the sense of Spanish well enough to translate the full
dimension of it into English—the look of the people, the sound of
pack burros rustling through the mesquite, the smell and taste of
tortillas and dusty roads. Riley loses little in translation, and when
one reads closely he can almost hear the telling of it.

The *cuentos* themselves have a venerable past, and scholars
have variously and theoretically traced their ancestry as far back
as the Indo-Europeans or the Asian Indians or the Egyptians. The
Brothers Grimm collected the same sorts of tales in Germany in the
early nineteenth century as Riley did on the Border in the twentieth,
as the reader can see by comparing Grimm's "Cinderella" with
Aiken's "La Cenicienta Huasteca" or "Seven at One Blow!" with
"Don Juan Zurumbete." The Anglo-Saxon Beowulf has gotten to
Mexico in the form of Juan Oso, and Uncle Remus's tar baby shows
up in "Sister Fox and Brother Coyote." Western civilization's folklore continues on the Borderland.

The characteristics of Riley Aiken's Mexican *cuentos* are the
same that can be found in the Old World wonder tales or, as they
are popularly called, fairy tales (with no fairies). The stories are
usually about the young or the poor or the weak and about their
struggles against outrageous odds which they overcome by passing
seemingly impossible tests in order to gain wealth, a princess, or
some sort of room at the top. With the help of ants and *brujas* and
all sorts of magical apparatus the protagonist overcomes these ob-
stacles and is successful. These stories are the underdogs' responses
to social dominance; because they can't make it in the pecking
order they need literary heroes who can. The youngest child turns
out to be the best, and the poor man tricks the rich man out of
his wealth, and the audience departs satisfied.

The literary devices of the *cuento* are the tried and true ones
used by the world's oldest tellers of tales. There is much repetition

of words and phrases and incidents to establish order and familiarity, and the incidents are written in parallel lines of structure. In "Blanca Flor" the hero's question and the three hermits' answers are always cast in the same form, and the episodes of Juan's three increasingly splendid appearances in the jail cell in "Tata Juan Pescador" are expectable and satisfying parallel incidents.

Cuento characters are more or less flat and represent the good guys against the bad, an ancient motif that goes back to the never-ending struggle between fertility and sterility. The youngest brother is better to his poor parents than the elder two in "Juan and the Bony One," but he is a simply defined character who is all good and who experiences no internal conflict in his journey to success, even when with poetic justice his evil brothers are dragged to death by wild mules. As in early Greek drama, only two or three characters appear in the action at one time. More than this would be too complicated for the storyteller to handle.

Although there may be several stories within the framework of one story, as in "The Parrot Tale-teller," the story line is straight to the end and uncomplicated by subplots, flashbacks, or digressions, again mainly because this would make the story too complicated to tell—or listen to. The stories and the episodes within the stories are plotted according to traditional five-part plot structure: situation, exciting force, rising action, climax, and falling action, in which the good are rewarded, the evil punished, and the moral made obvious.

We have to have our stories. We have to break loose from our mortal coils and charge vicariously into literary adventures. We yearn for tales as strongly as children at bedtime or Scheherazade's husband-king or the wife in Riley's "The Parrot Tale-teller." Stories are as necessary for our social equanimity as they were for the lords and ladies bound together by the plague in Boccaccio's *Decameron* or the pious pilgrims whom Chaucer sent to Canterbury.

In storytelling there is very little that is new. Good guys were beating out bad guys and Cinderellas were marrying princes in the very childhood of the oral tradition. Tests and trials and giants and stepmothers posed the same problems for heroes then as they did for the Juans of the Mexican *cuentos* and as they do now for the superheroes of Saturday morning television. The characters of

Grimm's *märchen* and Aiken's *cuentos* are no flatter than Starsky and Hutch, and the plots were no less contrived, held no fewer overheard conversations or last-minute rescues. The continuum of unsophistication has been maintained even into our own literate generation.

But there is a simplicity and a feeling of the earth in Riley Aiken's *Mexican Folktales from the Borderland* that put them outside and beyond the plasticity of most of our modern popular literary creations. In spite of the technical two-dimensionality of the *cuentos'* characters, they do have real flesh on their bones and dirt and sweat on their flesh and well-worn clothes hanging over all. The smell of mescal is there—and the feel of the dirt floors and the taste of the smoke from the cooking fire. Life—struggling, hungry life—can be felt behind the words, and the teller of tales walks in the dust of a real world.

FRANCIS EDWARD ABERNETHY

Texas Folklore Society
Stephen F. Austin State University
August, 1979

Preface

CONSCIOUSLY, I began collecting the tales here offered in 1929. Yet some of them date in my memory as far back as 1907. They are from the Mexican states of Tamaulipas, Nuevo León, Coahuila, and Chihuahua, all of the frontier, and from the Texas border counties of Cameron, Maverick, and Presidio. The little group of Kickapoo tales I heard one rainy evening at the *rancheria* of Kickapoo Indians called Nacimiento in the state of Coahuila.

The best stories I have were told me by one Santiago Garza, a teamster from the Sierra del Carmen region of Coahuila. He told me the stories of "Sister Fox and Brother Coyote," "The Tooth of Gold," and "The Dog That Ran to the Moon." The story of "La Cucaracha" came from a veritable Munchausen or Don Cacahuate named Doroteo living at a ranch thirty miles above Brownsville, Texas. He told me the parrot tale also.

I am grateful, primarily, to these individuals who passed these tales on to me; but I'm afraid the stories would not have found their way into print had it not been for Dr. E. R. Sims, J. Frank Dobie, Allen Maxwell, Wilson M. Hudson, and Mody C. Boatright. Many thanks to these friends and to my wife, Beulah, for her typing of the manuscript.

RILEY AIKEN

mexican folktales from the borderland

Chapter One

⤸ A TIME FOR EVERYTHING

"Mamacita, tell us a story," said Juanito. "This is no time for stories, *hijito*," responded the mother. "For instance, it is about time that you fill this tub with water so I can finish the washing and get the clothes on the bushes to dry."

"First a story, *mamacita*, then the water," teased the boy.

"This is no time for stories, Juanito. You must learn to be patient." Then, with a laugh, she continued, "If once upon a time people had been patient, none of us would have to die and stay dead; but, just as a worm changes into a butterfly, we would come from death slightly changed and would still continue to live."

"*Más, madrecita*; tell the rest of it," said Juanito.

"Well, Solomon, the wisest of all men, discovered just how it could be done. He told his most faithful servant that on a certain day he would die. 'You must wrap me in a certain way, and after I have been three weeks in the grave you must dig me up and unwrap me. After having spent that time in the sleep of death, I shall come alive again,' said Solomon.

"*Bueno, pues*, the people missed Solomon. They began to ask questions and they wanted to know why he was no longer on his throne.

3

" 'He is visiting another kingdom,' said the faithful servant. 'Within three weeks he will return.'

"At first the people were satisfied with the answer to their questions but soon a rumor swept the kingdom like a plague. It was told that the servant had murdered their ruler, and before he could escape from the kingdom to wait for the three weeks to pass, he was captured by a mob. The people demanded to see their king without delay.

"Now, if you had been the servant, Juanito, what would you have done?"

"I would have told them all about it," said the boy.

"I forgot to say that Solomon had asked that no one be told. In that case, Juanito, just what would you have done?"

"I don't know," said the boy.

"Very well, while you are thinking about it you may fill this tub with water," said the mother.

Juanito, very thoughtful, sat for a moment. Then he sprang to his feet and quickly filled the tub. "Now tell, *madrecita*; what did the faithful servant do?" he asked.

"He told the people it wasn't time for Solomon's return. They asked to know where the king had gone and the servant, refusing to tell, was threatened with death.

" 'Tell us,' they said, 'or we shall kill you.'

"The servant realized that if he told them, Solomon would never come alive again. He knew, too, that if he didn't tell, both he and his king would be dead forever. So he took them to the grave, showed them their ruler, and told them the story. The people were heartbroken and wept and prayed for forgiveness, but little good this did. They had not been patient with time, and just for that the secret of coming alive from death was lost forever and ever.

"And now, if you had waited until some other time, perhaps this story would have been better," said the mother.

⤳ EL PÁJARO CÚ

IT WAS WHEN GOD MADE THE WORLD.
When he created the birds, he first made them and then feathered them. This would have been wise except that a scarcity of feathers

left one little creature completely unclothed. This was Pájaro Cú. Yet he, Pájaro Cú, didn't mind in the least and went about from day to day as innocent as the dawn and as naked as the palm of your hand.

"What is to be done with him?" asked the owl.

"Poor thing," said the dove.

"Shocking," screamed the peafowl. And everyone agreed that it was shocking, a pity, and that something should be done.

"I move," said the owl, "that we each chip in a feather. None will miss so little, and yet all together will make him a splendid coat."

All agreed to this and were at the point of contributing, when the peafowl began to wail. "No—, no—, no—," she screamed, "he would then be so vain we could never manage him. Think of what you are doing; think of how beautiful he would be. His coat would contain red from the redbird, green from the parrot, black from the crow, white from the swan, gold from the canary, and silver from the guinea. No, no, it will never do, for he will burst with pride."

"We can't leave him this way," said the jackdaw. "He would disgrace the whole republic of birds."

"Yes," said the owl, "he must be clothed. If it is agreed, we will give him a feather, and I will go bond for him."

All the birds from the most common to the rarest contributed, and presently the Pájaro Cú was dressed beyond all description.

He walked to the fountain, gave one look at his magnificent self, and said, "Why do I associate with such birds? I will leave."

Thereupon he flew straight up into the blue of the heavens. Señor Owl followed but to no avail. He was too heavy, and Pájaro Cú was too light. He returned completely exhausted, only to face an angry mob.

"You were to go bond," said the rooster. "You have betrayed us."

"What do you plan to do, Mr. Owl?" asked the crow.

"What do I propose to do? What can be done, may I ask?"

Thereupon the birds flew at him, and it was with many wounds he escaped to a small hole in the side of a hill.

Three days passed, and it seemed he would die of hunger. Then a visitor called at the cave.

"Cu-rut, cu-rut," said he.

"Come in, Señor Roadrunner," said the owl.

"I have brought you a lizard, Señor Owl."

"*Muchas gracias*, Señor Paisano. I am indeed glad that I have at least one friend. Tell me, Señor Paisano, what am I to do?"

"Stay here; don't leave. Señor Cuervo has sworn to kill you."

"But I can't stay here," said the owl. "I must leave this hole in the ground. Tonight, while Señor Crow is asleep, I shall go to the swamps, and I will never cease hunting until I shall have found the Pájaro Cú."

"I will help," said the paisano. "While you search the woods and swamps by night, I will watch the roads by day."

And thus it has been ever since, that Señor Roadrunner keeps an eye on the roads and calls, "Cu-rut, cu-rut."

And in the woods at night the owl calls, "Cú, Cú, Cú, Cú, Cú."

⌐ SISTER FOX AND BROTHER COYOTE

FOR WEEKS 'MANA ZORRA HAD BEEN stealing a chicken each night from a ranch not far from her abode, when one night she found a small man standing near the opening she had made in the wire of the chicken house. The man was only a figure of wax put there by the *caporal* to frighten the thief. 'Mana[1] Zorra, unaware of this, was afraid; but, being very hungry, she decided to speak to the little man and ask permission to borrow a chicken.

"*Buenas noches*," said 'Mana Zorra.

There was no answer.

"He is either too proud to speak or doesn't hear," said the fox to herself. "If he isn't *mal criado* [ill-bred], then he didn't hear. I'll speak to him again."

Going nearer the wax man, she said, "*Buenas noches*, señor."

The little man made no response whatsoever; and the fox, after sizing him up from feet to head, decided that she had been insulted.

"*Ay*, the things I'm going to tell this *hombrecito*," said she. "He shall speak to me this time or I will slap his face."

She walked up to the figure and shouted at the top of her voice, "Step aside, please, and let me pass."

---

[1] *'Mana*, abbreviation of *hermana* (sister).

The wax man stubbornly stood his ground and refused to speak.

"*'Ora verás cómo yo te hago a un la'o* [now you shall see how I make you move to one side]," said 'Mana Zorra.

She struck the little man in the face, and much to her surprise her foot was caught and held fast.

"Let me go!" shouted 'Mana Zorra, "or I shall hit you again."

The wax man refused to let go and 'Mana Zorra hit him full in the face with a hard right swing. The result was that this foot too, like the other, was caught and held.

"*Ay, cómo eres abuzón,*"[2] grumbled 'Mana Zorra. "Listen, *amigo*, either you let me go or I shall give you a kicking you will never forget."

The wax man was not impressed by the threat and refused to let go. 'Mana Zorra made good her word as to the kicking, but the little man didn't seem to mind at all and added insult to injury by holding her hind feet too.

"I'll bite," she threatened; "I'll bite." And quickly she bit the neck of the wax figure, only to find herself caught not only by four feet but by her mouth as well.

"You think you have me," she scolded. "All right, how do you like this for a belly buster?" She pushed him so hard with her stomach that both of them fell rolling to the ground.

Just then who should appear on the scene but 'Mano[3] Coyote?

"What are you doing there, 'Mana Zorra?" he asked.

"Oh, nothing," she answered. "This Christian and I have come to blows over a chicken. I have a contract with the *ranchero* which provides me a hen a night, but this little fellow can't read and has made up his mind to interfere. Hold him for me, 'Mano Coyote, and I will get a hen for both of us."

The coyote, a gullible fellow, caught the wax man in a clinch and held tight until she stole a hen and escaped into the chaparral. Then, much to his chagrin, he found that he had been tricked and as a result would likely lose his life.

Dawn found 'Mano Coyote struggling with the wax man, and he was there and still fighting when the *caporal* arrived.

[2] A provincialism meaning *an abusive person.*

[3] *'Mano,* abbreviation of *hermano* (brother).

"*A' amiguito*," said the *caporal*. "This is what I have been wanting to find out for a long time. So it is you, Señor Coyote? And I had always thought you my friend. If you wanted a hen to eat, why didn't you come to me like a gentleman and ask for her? However, though greatly disappointed in you, I will give you another chance."

The *caporal* freed the coyote from the wax man and placed him in a little room with one broken window.

"Don't jump through this window till I call you," said the ranch foreman to the coyote. "My dogs will catch and kill you. Wait until I tie them up and get us a snack to eat. Then when I call, '*Al ataque!*' jump through the window and come to the kitchen."

The *caporal* heated water and poured it into a large pot that he had placed beneath the window. Then he called, "*Al ataque!* [come and get it!]"

And coyote jumped through the window and fell into the pot of boiling water. It was surely a miracle that saved his life, but the scalding water took the hair from his body and several toenails from his feet.

"*Ay, ay,*" said 'Mano Coyote, as he crept with flinching feet and sore hide through the thicket. "'Mana Zorra will pay for this. If I ever see her again I will kill her and eat her up."

Thus went 'Mano Coyote through the brush, whining and swearing vengeance until he reached a *laguna*. There before him lay the fox, gazing at something in the water.

"Now I have you," cried the coyote. "Now you are to pay for your smart trick."

"Don't kill me, 'Mano Coyotito," pleaded the fox. "Look, I was placed here to watch this cheese."

"What cheese?" asked the coyote.

The moon was full, and the reflection lay at the bottom of the *laguna*.

"There," said the fox, pointing at the reflection. "If you will watch it for me I will get us a chicken. However, be on guard lest the cheese slip beneath the bank."

"I'll watch it for you," said the coyote, "but don't be long. I'm dying for a chicken to eat."

'Mano Coyote had waited and watched several hours, when he saw the cheese slipping beneath the western bank of the *laguna*.

"Hey, Señor Cheese, don't go away," he called. "If you run away, I'll catch you and eat you up."

While 'Mano Coyote talked, the cheese continued to slip away. The coyote, fearing it would escape, sprang into the *laguna* and was soaked and chilled to the marrow before he reached the bank again.

"'Mana Zorra will pay for this," he howled. "Wherever I find her I shall kill her and eat her up."

The coyote had hunted the fox several days when at last he found her lying on her back in a small cave beneath a cropping of boulders. She was sound asleep.

"A', 'Mana Zorrita," hissed the coyote to the fox, "now I shall eat you up."

"Don't eat me, 'Mano Coyotito," begged the fox. "Look! When I went to get a hen, the *caporal* asked me to lie here and hold the world on my feet to keep it from falling down. He has gone to get more help and will be back soon to fix it. *Ay de mí*, 'Mano Coyote, I'm hungry. I know where there is a hen, but she will likely be gone when the *caporal* returns. *Ay de mí*, 'Mano Coyote, I'm hungry."

"I'm hungry, too," said the coyote. "Look, 'Mana Zorra, move over to one side. I'll hold the world on my feet if you will hurry and fetch us a hen."

"Good," said the fox. "But take care that the world doesn't fall and come to an end."

"I'll hold it," said the coyote, lying on his back and pushing up with all the strength of his four feet. "But hurry; I'm hungry."

The fox escaped, and the coyote remained beneath the rock for several hours until he was almost paralyzed by the increasing weight of the world.

At last, being unable longer to stand the pain of his cramped position, he said, "If it is going to fall, then let it fall. I'm quitting this job."

He sprang from beneath the ledge and ran into the clearing. The rock didn't fall, and the world showed no signs of coming to an end.

"*Ay, ay*," said he, "'Mana Zorra shall pay for this. If I ever catch her I shall kill her and eat her up."

At last the fox was found hiding beneath a large bush near a *gicotera.*[4]

"*A*', 'Mana Zorra," he cried, "you have played your last trick, for now I'm going to eat you up."

"Don't eat me, 'Mano Coyotito," begged the fox. "Look! I was on my way to get the chicken when a schoolteacher offered me pay to watch a class of boys."

"Where are the boys?" asked the coyote.

"There, before us; it is their schoolroom."

"Where is the money?" asked the coyote further.

"In my pocket," said the fox, as she rattled some broken pieces of porcelain.

"*Pos*, that's good," said the coyote. "What are you going to do with it?"

"I'm going to buy you a pair of trousers, and a skirt for myself."

"Your idea is good," observed the coyote. "However, you must leave some money with which to purchase food."

"Certainly," said the fox. "I shall buy us a chicken apiece. But why did you mention food, 'Mano Coyote? *Ay, ay de mí*, I'm dying of hunger."

"I'm hungry, too," said the coyote.

"Look!" said the fox. "Watch these boys for me and I'll fetch the hen right away."

"*Cómo no?*" said the coyote. "Only hurry, 'Mana Zorra."

The fox saved her hide again, and the coyote was left with the devil to pay; for the schoolroom was a hornets' nest, and the boys weren't pupils but a lively lot of hornets.

The coyote sat listening to the hum of pupils reading their lessons, when he noticed that the sound had ceased. "They are loafing on me," he said. "I'll shake them up a bit."

He shook them up, and this would have been his last adventure had he not found a *laguna* into which to dive and escape the swarm of hornets.

"*Ay, ay*," wailed the coyote. "'Mana Zorra shall pay for this. Wherever it is that I find her I shall eat her up, hide and hair."

At last 'Mana Zorra was found in a *carrizal*—a reed swamp.

[4] *Gicotera*, a rat's nest at the roots of a bush; but Santiago Garza told me that a kind of bee makes its nest in a *gicotera*.

'Mano Coyote had not forgotten the hornets' sting, the moon cheese, the world trick, and the wax man.

"Now there shall be no more foolishness," said he. "'Mana Zorra must die."

"Don't eat me," pleaded the fox. "Don't eat me, 'Mano Coyotito. Look! I was on my way to get the hens, when I met a bridegroom. He invited me to be godmother at his wedding. I felt it would be bad to refuse; and now that you are here you and I shall be *padrino* and *madrina*. You know how it is at these weddings. There is always plenty to eat and drink, and when it comes to chicken, there is none better in the world than that served at a wedding feast. *Ay, ay*, I'm hungry, 'Mano Coyotito."

"*Pos, sí*," said the coyote; "I'm hungry, too. But where is the wedding party?"

"They are to pass at any time now," said the fox. "You stay here, and I'll see if they are coming. If you hear popping and cracking you will know it is the fireworks shot by the friends of the couple. I shall be back soon."

'Mana Zorra slipped around the canebrake and set fire to it in first one place and then another. 'Mano Coyote heard the popping and cracking and began to dance with joy.

"*Taco Talaco*," said he, "here they come. *Taco Talaco, ay, Taco Talaco*, what a hot time there will be."

He discovered his mistake too late. The fire had trapped him completely, and so ended the career of 'Mano Coyote the dupe, shouting "*Taco Talaco*" and dancing at his own funeral.

⟿ A BOOM IN GUARACHE LEATHER

THERE ONCE LIVED TWO MEN WHO lived in Coyame. One was rich, and the other poor. The rich man counted his cows on an adding machine, while the poor man needed only one finger of one hand to keep track of his. Yet, Don Pedro Carrasco, the man of wealth and importance, was envious of the poor man, José Días, whose cow was large, fat, and never dry.

"José," said Don Pedro, "I will give you one hundred pesos for your cow."

"*Pos*, señor," said the *peladito* (ragged fellow), "she is my only possession; and if she were sold my family and I would starve *sin remedio.*"

"I will give you ten cows in exchange for yours," said Don Pedro.

"Pardon, señor," said José, "my one cow is never dry, and she gives ten times more milk than your ten cows would give."

Don Pedro walked away without further comment, but those who saw the anger in his face felt that José would, ere long, have much cause for regret.

Three days later the two men met on the *plazuela.*

"*Buenos días,* José," said Señor Carrasco with such a show of courtesy that the *peladito* was thrown completely off his guard. "Are your *asaderos* selling well?"

"*Sí,* señor," said the poor man, "with God's help I sell enough cheese to furnish my family with food and clothing. I have no cause for complaint, *gracias a Dios.*"

"It seems a pity to spend one's life barely living, José. With *guarache* leather selling in Aldama at ten pesos a pair, inside two days you could be a man of wealth. You know, *amigo,* that beyond the mountains the people have only this week learned to wear sandals. Your cow would make one hundred pairs of *guaraches,* and ten times one hundred would bring one thousand pesos. You see," continued Don Pedro, "you see, a good friend to tip one off and a bit of figuring and a bit of common sense are all one needs these days to make money out of no money at all."

"Is it really true," asked José, "that in Aldama *guaraches* are ten pesos a pair?"

"*Hombre,* would I say so if they were not?" responded Don Pedro. "Go ask Lupe Aguilar, the brother-in-law of Cuca Ramírez. It was only this morning that he told me, and this very day I shall kill some cows and sell their hides for *guaraches.*"

The trick worked. Within an hour José Días was no longer content with the even trend of things. "One thousand pesos," he mused. "Just fancy, the *vieja* could have fine clothes, the daughters the many things they need, and I would no longer have to work. A thousand pesos! *Figúrese no más!* Just figure that to yourself!" The *peladito* became such a victim of illusions that before nightfall he had killed his cow, skinned her, and cut the hide into small strips the size of the sole of a man's foot. Without caring for the meat in any manner, he left that very night for Aldama.

Bright and early the following morning on a street in Aldama two policemen were startled by a strange vendor's call.

"*Guaraches!*" was the cry. "*Guaraches!* Ten pesos a pair."

"Is he drunk or crazy?" asked one of the policemen.

"We will take him to the *presidente municipal* and soon find out," said the other.

José told his story, and everyone except the *presidente* laughed.

"Carrasco has caused you to make a fool of yourself my friend," said he. "Your rawhide isn't worth three pesos, much less a thousand. Here, take this coin, buy yourself a taco or two and leave Aldama."

Mechanically José accepted the gift and, without bothering to shoulder his bundle of *guarache* leather, took to the street.

"Now there will be no clothes for the *vieja*," said he, "no gifts for the daughters, and now of all times there will be no rest for myself. What a fool I've been!"

Just then a street vendor called: "*Máscaras! Máscaras del diablo!*"

José turned, saw a cartload of masks, and on the very top a devil's face so red-eyed, sharp-eared, wolfish, and weird that he decided to buy it. He gave the *presidente*'s coin to the vendor, took the mask, and placing it beneath his shirt, proceeded on his way out of town.

Night overtook him on the mountain slopes west of Coyame. With night came a cold north wind, and the poor man was at the point of freezing when, to the left of the road, he saw a campfire. He approached it and found ten men seated on ten leather bags around the blaze.

"May I warm myself?" asked José.

A minute passed before a word was spoken. At last, however, one of the men told him to come near the fire and make himself comfortable.

José was too cold just then to care who his hosts might be. Later, however, while warming his hands at the blaze, he studied them one by one and concluded that they were bandits.

Suddenly a noise was heard. The men jumped to their feet.

"What is it?" asked José.

"One of the saddle horses staked in the brush," said the captain. "We thought it might be Indians. A tribe has been on our trail since sunrise."

José figured it would be well to leave, but the warmth of the fire and the rushing of the bitter norther through the catsclaw brush, plus the fact that he was very tired, caused him to delay and finally to abandon any intention of leaving the fire for the night.

One after the other, the bandits spread their sarapes side by side near the fire, lay down, and went to sleep. The night grew colder and the wind stronger. José was too busy keeping warm to think of sleep. For an hour he spent the time turning first his face and then his back to the fire. He got more wood from the brush, built a larger blaze, and still he thought that surely his nose would freeze.

He was warming his back and wondering just how he could make himself more comfortable, when suddenly he remembered the mask. He placed it over his face. His nose, ears, and cheeks soon were warm again, but his hands were cold. He turned to the fire, reached out to the blaze, and was rubbing his hands and groaning when the bandit nearest the blaze awoke.

Now, this fellow hadn't been a good man, and what he saw looking at him through the flames and smoke paralyzed him with fear. Presently he eased over to the nearest bandit and touched him with his elbow. This fellow also, like the first, was scared stiff and could hardly breathe. One by one the bandits awoke until the last man, the captain, was nudged by his neighbor.

The captain had had a bad dream. He dreamed he was dead and the devil had come to get him. When he awoke to find himself free to run, run he did, calling to the men as he went, "*Pronto, muchachos!* Run for your lives!"

José was unaware that they were awake until he saw them running away and heard the captain screaming at the top of his voice for his men to run. "Indians!" he thought, and followed hot on the heels of the bandits. One of them saw him coming and yelled, "He's coming, *muchachos!* Hurry, hurry!"

José ran so fast the mask slipped over his eyes and he stumbled and fell. He lost no time in getting to his feet again, but he had lost his sense of direction for the moment. He listened. There was no sound anywhere.

"Strange," said he as he fumbled the mask. "Strange. I wonder. *Válgame Dios!* It must have been the mask. I must call these fellows back and explain."

He followed in the direction they had fled until he came to a large precipice; and there, a hundred feet below, he heard a bandit groaning. They had all fallen over the cliff and were dead or dying.

José returned to the fire and picked up one of the ten leather pouches. Greatly to his surprise it was full of gold pieces. He opened another. It, too, was full of gold; and so it was with the rest of them—all full of gold. He tied the pouches in pairs yoked together, and put them on five of the saddle horses that had been staked by the bandits. Then, mounting another horse, he set out for his hut and, with the ten sacks of gold all safe, reached it before dawn.

At ten o'clock that morning the one he-gossip of the *villa* came nosing around.

"*Buenos días,* José," he said.

"*Buenos días,* señor."

"They tell me you killed your cow, *amigo.*"

"*Sí,* señor! I killed her."

"They tell me, José, that you tried to sell her hide for *guarache* leather at ten pesos a pair," added the gossip with a hint of honeyed derision.

"*Mire, amigo,*" said José, "Don Pedro Carrasco did me a great injustice."

"Don't tell me that," said the man.

"Yes," continued José, "he told me to sell the hide at ten pesos a pair; but fortunately I met a friend in Aldama who tipped me off to the fact that *guarache* leather was selling at twenty pesos a pair. Look."

He took a handful of gold from his right pocket. "What do you think of that?" he said with a wee small hint of boasting. "And if that isn't convincing, look."

He drew another handful of gold from his left pocket.

"Look, *amigo,*" he went on, "this is yours. Take it. Certainly, all of it, my friend. Only do me one little favor. Don't tell Don

Pedro Carrasco about it. I am going to buy his cows, kill them all, and sell their hides. *Figúrese, hombre* [consider, man]; at twenty pesos a pair for *guaraches*, with all those cows I shall soon be the richest man in the whole republic. But remember, not a word to Don Pedro Carrasco."

What were promises to the town's he-gossip? Within thirty minutes Don Pedro knew the whole story. By nightfall he had rounded up and killed all his cows, and at dawn the following morning he was in Aldama with the first wagonload of *guarache* leather.

"*Guaraches!*" he cried. "*Guaraches!* Twenty pesos a pair."

"Listen," said one of the policemen to the other. "He's back again."

"No," responded the other officer, "it's someone else."

"Is he drunk or crazy?" asked the first.

"Crazy, likely, and twice as crazy as the other. Let's take him to the *presidente municipal*."

Don Pedro told his story, and everyone laughed, including the *presidente*. In fact the *presidente* laughed himself into a fit of coughing; and it was some time before he could regain enough composure and dignity to speak as an impartial judge. "*Todos andamos cojeando del propio pie,*[5] Don Pedro, and you have limped into bad business on account of avarice. *En su mismo pecado lleva Vd. la penitencia* [your sin carries its own penance]. And since justice was so prompt in this case, I feel there is nothing for me to do except to give you your liberty and a bit of advice. Remember this: *Para pagar es corresponder* [the way to pay is to return the favor]. Give my regards to your friend José Días, and on your way out, *hombre, cante por no ponerse a llorar* [sing to keep from crying]."

José and his family are wealthy now, and they have given much money to the *santitos* and the poor.

---

[5] "We all go limping, each on his own foot." This is a proverb meaning that each person reacts according to his own defects.

⤶ THE SON OF TATA JUAN PESCADOR

NOT FAR FROM A LARGE CITY, ONCE upon a time, lived a fisherman and his family. Though there were only three of them and the father worked very hard, they were very poor.

One evening at sunset a carriage drawn by six white horses stopped at Tata Juan's door. A blond young woman, as pretty as a princess, stepped down from the carriage and asked Tata Juan for lodging.

"It would be a great honor," said Tata Juan, "but we are very poor and have only this one little hut with its one little room."

The young woman insisted, and the poor family felt compelled to take her in.

Upon leaving the following morning, the young woman announced that she was going to the *centro* of the city to attend the fair. "I shall return," she said.

Upon her return to the hut that evening she met the third member of the fisherman's family. It was Juanito, the little son. His clothes were torn and in patches, his hair was long, and his face and hands were dirty.

"Give me this boy," said the young woman.

"We can't do that," said Tata Juan, "for he is our only child and some day will be our only support."

"Look, Tata Juan," said the beautiful young woman, "I am a fairy from the fairy town of Canela. Give me Juanito and you will never regret it. Tomorrow evening when I return from the fair, I shall expect your answer."

The following day there was much argument in the little family between father and mother. By nightfall, however, they had agreed to give their son Juanito to the fairy of Canela.

"I am greatly indebted to you," said the fairy upon learning their decision. "In partial recompense I will present you with this magic vase. When you need money, say only the words 'Componte, jarrito!'[6] and it will be filled with coins immediately."

The next morning the fairy took Juanito to a bath and cleaned him up. Then she called in a barber and a tailor, and within less

---

[6] Something like "Do your stuff, little vase!"

time than it takes to say it Juanito was transformed into a little prince.

"We shall go now," said the fairy.

The six white horses and carriage returned. Tata Juan and the *pescadora* (fisherwoman) were told good-bye, and soon Juanito and the fairy had gone.

The way to Canela was long and led through a desert. Midday was warm and Juanito began to drowse.

"Don't fall asleep," said the fairy.

Juanito, however, was no match for slumber and soon was sound asleep.

At sunset he awoke; he was no longer in the carriage, but alone on the desert. He was no longer a little prince, but the dirty street urchin of yesterday.

"What shall I do?" thought he. "Which way shall I go?"

He sat down and removed a *guarache* from his foot.

"I have heard," said he, "that it is well to throw a hide into the air and follow the direction it points. Since I have no hide, I shall throw my *guarache*, which is made of hide."

He threw the sandal, flip-coin fashion, and it landed with toe pointing north. Juanito slipped his bare foot back into it and set out walking north.

He had gone but a little way when he heard sounds that chilled his blood. Being unable to make out what they were, he crept cautiously forward through the brush. At last he came to a small opening; and immediately before him in the center of the clearing were a lion, an eagle, and an ant fighting over a dead cow.

The lion saw Juanito and called to him.

"Come here, boy. We must have someone to divide this kill for us, for otherwise we shall never reach an agreement."

Juanito was afraid, but he dared not disobey. He gave the head to the ant, the loins to the eagle, and the remainder to the lion.

"You have divided well," said the lion. "Now you must have your fee. Come, pull a hair from my mane."

"There is one of my feet," said the ant.

"What are you going to give?" said the lion to the eagle.

The latter did not answer but flew away.

"What shall I do with this hair and foot?" asked Juanito.

"If you are in trouble," said the lion, "and need my help, hold the hair between your forefinger and thumb and say, '*Dios y mi buen león* [God and my good lion].' If it is the ant you need, say '*Dios y mi buena hormiga* [God and my good ant].'"

"*Bueno*," said Juanito, "then I shall start with you, Señor León."

Thereupon he held the mane hair between the thumb and forefinger and said, "*Dios y mi buen león!*"

"At your service," said the lion.

"Take me to the town of Canela," said the boy.

They walked toward the north until late and pitched camp for the night near a tree.

Presently a voice came from the branches overhead. "It is I, the eagle," said the voice. "Don't leave camp tomorrow morning until a cow is driven here. I shall take you to the town of Canela, but we must have meat."

At dawn a beef was driven into camp. The ant stung its foot and during the pause the lion sprang on it and killed it.

The meat not consumed by the four was jerked and bagged; and at noon Juanito, with the meat, climbed on the eagle's back.

"When I call '*Carne*,'" said the eagle, "you must give me meat. That way I shall not have to come to earth. Hold tight; here we go."

The eagle had called "*Carne*" seven times and eaten the entire supply, when it lit on the bank of a lagoon.

"Sh! quiet," said he. "A monster lives in the mud beneath this lagoon. We must kill him before we can continue our journey. Call the lion and the ant."

The boy first took the lion hair and said, "*Dios y mi buen león*," and then with the little foot of the ant held between the thumb and forefinger he said, "*Dios y mi buena hormiga.*"

Both lion and ant came immediately, but not a second too soon; for a large wave was already rolling shoreward from the lagoon. Puerco Espín, the monster, made for the boy but was attacked by the lion. The battle was fierce and both were badly wounded. The lion was forced to quit the fight to rest and pull poisonous barbs from his paws, but the Puerco Espín crawled back to the lagoon, rolled in the mud, and was cured of his wounds immediately.

For the second time he prepared to attack the boy, but before he reached him one foot was so paralyzed by the ant's sting he could not move a limb. Before the lion and eagle killed him, the latter said, "When we open him a snake will escape. Kill it quickly. A dove will come from the snake. I shall catch it and bring it to earth. Within the dove is an egg. We must kill the dove to get the egg. Then, boy, you are to carry the egg in your hand to the palace door at Canela, where you will find the guard distracted by the ant's sting. Break the egg on his head, and you will be received into the palace. If, however, by accident or otherwise the egg is broken beforehand, we shall all find ourselves by the carcass of the first beef in the center of the desert and the whole business will needs be repeated again."

All transpired as the eagle had said. The boy was careful with the egg, and after a flight of a few hours the eagle placed him at the palace door in the town of Canela. The ant had preceded them and had done his job well, for the guard was swearing and scratching his ankle. Juanito came near with the caution of a cat, broke the egg on the guard's head, and was received into the castle, given a good supper, and shown to his bed. He removed his clothes and crawled beneath the covers.

"You are now within the castle of Canela, Juanito," said a voice from beneath the bed. "It is I, the fairy of Canela, who speaks."

"I am homesick," said Juanito. "Take me to my father and mother."

"No, Juanito, they have been so busy with the *jarrito* they have forgotten you."

Juanito's heart could stand no more. "All the same, I am homesick. Take me back."

"Very well," said the fairy.

Next day the coach, drawn by the six white horses, stopped at the castle door. Juanito and the fairy took their seats and soon were on their way through the desert.

"Don't fall asleep," said the fairy.

However, Juanito was no match for slumber. He awoke that evening all alone in the middle of the desert. He lost no time in getting his directions and before dawn had reached the city of his birth.

In the absence of his son, Tata Juan Pescador had worked the magic vase day and night, had become fabulously rich, and had been elected governor. Pride got the better of him, and he decreed that no one was ever, under the penalty of death, to refer to him as Tata Juan Pescador.

Juanito knew nothing of this, and, not finding his parents at home, asked an old woman the whereabouts of Tata Juan Pescador.

"*Ay, hijito*," said she, "if you go about asking for Tata Juan Pescador you will be shot. Call at the city home of the *gobernador* and ask to see *el Señor Gobernador*."

Juanito did this and said he was the governor's son. Tata Juan Pescador said he had no son and had the boy arrested as an impostor. Juanito spent the night in a cell within the governor's mansion.

At early dawn a voice spoke through the bars of the windows. "The fairy of Canela sends you food that you may eat, a prince's suit that you may dress, and a *talega of reales*[7] that you may attend the fair. Go with the governor and spend the whole bag of *reales*. At twilight return to this cell."

Juanito dressed quickly and ate. An old woman came to his door with prison food; but when she saw a prince instead of a street urchin, she ran to the governor and asked him to go to the cell in person.

Tata Juan Pescador was frightened, released Juanito, and fell to his knees with apologies.

"That is all very well, Señor Gobernador," said Juanito. "We shall go to the fair."

They passed the day in the *centro*, spent all the *reales*, and returned at twilight to the mansion. It was against the governor's wish that the prince should sleep that night in the cell, but Juanito insisted on having his bed there.

At early dawn the voice spoke again through the bars of the window.

"The fairy of Canela sends you food that you may eat, a king's robe that you may dress, and a *talega* of *reales* that you may attend the fair. Go with the governor and spend the whole bag of money. At twilight, return to this cell."

Juanito, as he had done the day before, dressed quickly and

---

[7] One thousand dollars; a *real* is 12½ cents.

ate. Again came the old woman to the door, saw the king, and fled to the governor.

"I'm not so sure but that you'll be shot for this," said she. "A king is in the cell."

Tata Juan Pescador, in even more anxiety than the day before, hastened to release the king and apologize.

"That is all very well, Señor Gobernador," said Juanito. "Come, we shall go to the fair again."

The day was passed in the *centro*, the *reales* were all spent, and at twilight Juanito was in his cell again.

As on the two previous occasions, the voice spoke again through the bars of the window.

"The fairy of Canela sends you food that you may eat, an emperor's robe that you may dress, and a *talega* of *reales* that you may attend the fair. Go with the governor and spend the whole bag of money. At twilight do not return to the cell but make yourself known to your father, Tata Juan Pescador. Then at dawn on the day following, return to the town of Canela."

When the old woman came to the prison door, she fled to the governor and said, "Now I'm sure you'll be shot, for it is the emperor you have in prison."

Tata Juan Pescador was so frightened he could hardly stand. He apologized and released the emperor.

"That is all very well, Señor Gobernador," said Juanito. "Come, we shall attend the bullfight at the fair."

That evening Juanito did not return to the cell. Instead, he fell on his knees before his father and mother and revealed his name.

Tata Juan and the *pescadora* were hardly equal to the great joy that was theirs. The three of them—Tata Juan, the mother, and the son—sat up all night, and a little mouse heard Juanito tell them the story I have told you.

Juanito left his parents in a sea of tears when he set out for Canela, but the little mouse doesn't know whether he fell asleep in the desert or not.

> *Colorín colorado;*   *Colorín colorado;*
> *Que este cuento*   That this tale
> *Se ha acabado.*   Is ended.

Chapter Two

↳ REPAYING GOOD WITH EVIL

THIS WAS A WISE MAN WHO, WHILE walking along a path, found a serpent in a trap.

"Please let me out," begged the serpent. "It's wrong to keep me here."

"You are right," said the wise man. "It is wrong to keep one trapped." Thereupon he released the snake.

Immediately the serpent coiled about his benefactor and prepared to eat him.

"This is not right," said the wise man. "It is wrong to repay good with evil."

"Perhaps," replied the serpent, "but I am hungry."

"That I regret," said the wise man. "It is wrong to repay good with evil. Before you devour me, let's ask the opinion of someone else."

"That would only prolong your worry, for he would agree with me," said the serpent. "However, to please you, we will call a judge."

They spied a horse passing near. "Come here," called the wise man. "Come here, Señor Caballo. We want your opinion in a serious dispute."

The horse approached and heard impartially the pleas of each. "It is indeed not right for one to repay good with evil," said he. Then, fearing the wrath of the serpent, he added, "But on the other hand, *es la costumbre* [it is the custom] that good be repaid with evil. Behold myself, for example. Once I was young, had the best food, and was happy; and it was with my energy that my master became a rich man. Now that I am old, he has turned me out to starve. Yes, *es la costumbre* to repay good with evil."

Then they called the ox. "Brother Ox," said the serpent, "we have called you to hear our cause and give an opinion. My friend here contends that it is wrong to repay good with evil. What is your judgment?"

The ox looked the facts calmly in the face and meditated and chewed his cud. Then with a tired sigh he said, "Whether it is right or whether it is wrong is not the case. *Es la costumbre* to repay good with evil."

"Fine," said the serpent to the wise man. "Now I shall devour you."

"We are but little wiser than we were," pleaded the wise man. "Grant that we hear the opinion of one more judge."

Thereupon they called the coyote. "'Mano Coyote," said the wise man, "my friend the serpent contends that it is right to repay good with evil. *Qué dices?*"

"I had rather not say without due thought. I am just *gente corriente* [common folks], a wild animal from the chaparral. My judgment at best may be of little use. What is the trouble?"

The story was told how the snake was released by the wise man, and then how the former was wanting to devour the latter when the wise man said that it was not right to repay good with evil.

"That is not enough," said 'Mano Coyote. "I desire to study the case more in detail. Now just how was the serpent trapped? Show me where and show me the trap and show me just how he was fastened, for it might be that he was never trapped at all."

The serpent feared the suggestion that the trap was only a trick. He placed himself as the wise man had found him.

"Now is that really the way you were fastened in, Mr. Snake?" asked the coyote.

"It is," said the snake.

"Is that really the way he was caught?" he asked the wise man.

"It is," said the wise man.

"Then it is my judgment that the situation as it stands is better than it was when I found it. That is all and *he dicho* [I have spoken]."

"But it isn't right to leave him to die," said the wise man.

"If it isn't," said the coyote, "it's his own affair."

The wise man and the coyote walked away.

When out of hearing, the coyote said to the wise man, "Brother Wise Man, you will not deny that I have saved your life."

"No," said the wise man. "Though your decision was not definite, at least you saved my life. Look! I own a ranch near here. Come there at eight every morning from now on, after I have tied up the dog, and I shall give you a hen."

"Good!" said the coyote. "That is better; that is repaying good with good."

The coyote found life so easy he became lazy and took to strong drink, insisting that his appetite was bad and that he needed a *traguito* each morning before eating a hen. Then within a few days he complained that the *traguito* of *sotol* increased his appetite so much that one hen was not enough. The wise man was compelled to add a bottle of *sotol* and another hen to the daily menu.

"It seems," meditated the wise man, "that, after all, good is repaid with evil. It was right to give the coyote something, but now my friend is resorting to blackmail."

"And that isn't all," growled the dog. "Ere long he will call for another hen. I know him; he lives by his wits."

"That would be my ruin," said the wise man. "What should one do?"

"Put him off one day," said the dog; "then put me in the sack with the hens and when he calls for another chicken, let me out. I will attend to him."

Before long the coyote began to hint that one bottle of *sotol* and two hens were poor pay for the saving of a life. "It seems that you have forgotten that good must be repaid with good," said he to the wise man.

"It seems, 'Mano Coyote," answered the latter, "that you have forgotten that at one time you said one hen a day was enough."

"But time changes all. The first contract is now unsatisfactory," answered the coyote. "It is my desire now that I be paid three bottles of *sotol* and three hens daily."

"Very well," said the wise man, "tomorrow I shall begin the new arrangements."

The following morning at the appointed time the wise man came to the meeting place with three bottles of *sotol* and three sacks.

"*Ay, carray!* Toss me out a hen," yipped 'Mano Coyote.

This the wise man did. The coyote devoured her, feathers and all, and then drank another bottle of *sotol*.

"*Ay qué carray!*" he shouted. "Toss me out another hen."

The wise man released another hen. The coyote pounced upon her and ate her quicker than the first.

"*Caramba!*" he said. "With age and experience my appetite grows. Now give me the other bottle of *sotol*."

After finishing the third bottle, he shouted, "Let her out, *y viva La Revolución!*"

The wise man released the dog from the sack. The poor coyote was too drunk and stuffed to run. He was caught, but before the fangs of the dog had found their mark he called to the wise man, "It isn't right to repay good with evil. Call off your dog."

"Perhaps it isn't right," answered the wise man, "but *es la costumbre.*"

⤴ THE THREE COUNSELS

THIS WAS A BOY WHO RAN AWAY from home. Though at heart not bad, he had three habits that were by no means good, for he would stick to no purpose, was always asking about people's personal affairs, and would not control his temper.

Sí, señor, he ran away from home, but, do you know, he was hardly beyond the horizon when he left the highway for a trail, called to an old man to know his business, and flew into a rage when the latter did not answer.

Presently, however, the *viejito* spoke. "I am a peddler of advice," said he.

"What kind of advice?" asked the boy.

"It will cost you one peso to find out," was the answer.

The boy had only three pesos, but curiosity induced him to give one to the *viejito*.

"First," said the old man, "don't leave a highway for a trail."

"Is that what you call advice?" asked the boy. "You are a fraud."

"Don't you like that one?" asked the *viejito*. "Then give me another peso and lend an ear."

The boy reluctantly handed over the second of his three pesos and waited. "Second," said the *viejito*, "don't ask about things that don't pertain to you."

"*Mal ladrón*," shouted the boy, "for one peso I would kill you."

"Calm yourself, *hijito*," said the old man. "I have among my wares one more bit of advice you need. Will you buy it or not?"

The boy's curiosity was too much for him. He gave his last peso to the stranger and listened attentively for the third time.

"Don't lose your temper," laughed the old man, and before the boy could gather his wits, he had vanished into the chaparral.

Sad and empty of pocket, the youth continued on his way.

He took to the road again just as a stranger mounted on a large black horse galloped up.

"Where to, *joven*?" called he.

"To the city," said the boy.

"Then you need advice," responded the man. "Look, I will help you. One league up the road you will find a short cut. You will recognize it by my horse's tracks. It will save you many miles."

The boy thanked him and continued on his journey with the purpose of leaving the highway for the path. However, never being able to keep to a purpose, he disregarded the path.

At noon he came to a ranch house. A bandit sat beneath an arbor in front of it.

"*Pase, joven*," he called. "You are just in time for dinner."

The boy entered the house and took a chair at the table. He had waited no time when a servant placed before him a dish containing the head of a man. He was at the point of asking a question when he remembered suddenly one of his three costly bits of advice. "I had better ask no questions," thought he.

"Young man," said the bandit, "what do you think of this head?"

"It is a good head," replied the boy.

"Have you no questions?" queried the bandit.

"No, señor, none."

"Would you like to see some of my keepsakes?" asked the bandit.

"If it is your pleasure to show them," said the boy, "then it will be my pleasure to see them."

A closet was opened and the boy was shown many skeletons hanging by the neck.

"How do you like my men?" asked the host.

"They are good men," answered the boy.

"*Joven*," said the bandit, "I kill all my guests. These men, like you, each in his turn stepped across my threshold to have dinner with me. Each was shown a head, but, unlike you, they wanted to know all about it. Their curiosity brought them to their present condition. You, however, have asked nothing about things that do not concern you; and for that reason my servants will conduct you safely from the ranch. In my corral there are three mules and a horse. The mules will be loaded with gold, and the horse will be saddled. These are yours."

Six bags of gold were tied *mancornados* [in pairs] and placed on the mules. The boy mounted the horse and with the help of the servants was soon on the highway again. "Indeed," he said to himself, "it pays to keep to the main road, and it pays to ask no questions about things that do not concern me. Now I am rich."

"Halt!" called a voice from the roadside.

There stood a bandit with feet spread and arms crossed.

"What have you in those sacks?" he asked.

The boy was at the point of cursing with rage when he recalled the third bit of advice.

"It is a secret I prefer not to tell," he answered calmly.

"Speak or I will kill you," threatened the bandit.

"If you feel that is best," said the boy, "then follow your conscience."

"Ha!" said the man, "you are a wise boy. *Adiós*; may you have a pleasant journey."

This *joven* entered the city. Before many weeks had passed he had built and stocked the best store in town and was making barrels of money. Furthermore, he met and married a wealthy girl. However, the best of all was that she, too, did not leave the main road for a path, asked no questions about things that did not pertain to her, and always kept her temper.

⌐ LA CUCARACHA

JUAN DE TOLUCA HAD BEEN A GOOD man. Therefore it was to the gates of Paradise that he directed his steps upon leaving this life.

"*Buenos días,* San Pedro," said he. "*Con su permiso* I wish to enter here."

But before St. Peter gave his permission, he began asking questions. He wanted to know how much money Juan had, his name and age, and his religion. At last he asked, "What is your race?"

"*Mexicano,*" answered Juan.

"Well, that is too bad," said St. Peter. "We don't keep Mexicans here."

"Why?" asked Juan. "Isn't it enough that one has lived by the commandments and attended church?"

"Generally speaking, that is true," said St. Peter, "but the Lord has asked me to keep to the letter of the law. It is nowhere written in our constitution that heaven was made for Mexicans; therefore, I must ask that you step out of line and go to the regions below."

Juan was insistent, however. It had never been his plan to live in the infernal regions. Besides, he had gone to considerable expense upon leaving the vale of tears and had paid sixty pesos for a new hat. This useless expense San Pedro regretted sincerely, but he maintained that he could do nothing about the matter.

"Well, if I must take the other trail, I shall go," said Juan. "However, San Pedro, please do me one—and only one—favor."

"And what favor is that, Juan?"

"Permit me, please, to take one little peep at the City of Paradise."

San Pedro refused, saying that the memory of the sight of heaven would make hell hotter for him.

"You had better run along," he continued. "You are blocking the line."

Juan fell upon his knees and pleaded so earnestly that St. Peter
said, "Well, if that's all you want, have your way."

Thereupon he allowed the Mexican to stick his head through a
small opening in the gate of pearls.

Juan saw all that he had ever imagined he would see and even
more. He realized the bitter truth of St. Peter's warning that he
would regret the glimpse and determined quickly to resort to cunning. He removed his hat, and at a moment when St. Peter's back
was turned, sent it rolling down the main street of heaven.

"My hat fell off!" he cried. "*Ay, ay, ay, sombrero de mis
entrañas!* I will never leave this place without the sombrero so dear
to my affections."

St. Peter was greatly perplexed. Some contend he had taken a
liking to the Mexican. However this may be, the fact is he opened
the gate and bade Juan get his hat and hurry back.

Once in Paradise, however, Juan found it convenient to lose
himself in the great crowds of angels; and since St. Peter was having trouble at the gate, the illegal entrance was overlooked.

Everything was going smoothly in God's kingdom until one
day an angel asked to speak privately to the Lord.

"What do you want?" asked Nuestro Señor.

"No, nothing, Señor," replied the angel reverently, "except,
Señor, I have lost a ring, and I suspect someone of having . . ."

"Sh!" said the Lord. "Not so loud. Never mention the ring
again."

The angel bowed, apologized, and left immediately.

Three days later another angel asked for a private interview
with the Lord.

"What do you want?" asked the Lord.

"No, nothing," said the angel, "only, Señor, I have lost a diamond brooch, and I suspect someone of having . . ."

"Sh!" said the Lord. "Not so loud; it will ruin the reputation of
my place. Go now and never mention the brooch again."

Three days passed and still another angel asked to speak to the
Lord in private.

"What do you want?" asked Nuestro Señor.

"No, nothing," said the angel, "only, Señor, just this morning I
lost my earbobs, and . . ."

"I know," said the Lord; "I know."

Nuestro Señor looked sad and perplexed. At last, he said in a whisper, "Do you know, I believe there is a Mexican in heaven."

He went immediately to St. Peter. "Don't waste your breath, St. Peter," said he. "It isn't a question of denial. A Mexican is among us, and we must find some way to rid the place of him without a scandal. Look, the Texan is his neighbor. He knows the Mexicans; go quickly to the devil and borrow one for a few moments."

Presently the Lord and St. Peter were asking all manner of questions.

"What are his weak points?" asked Nuestro Señor.

"Well, well," said the Texan.

"Ah, ah," said Nuestro Señor, "no spitting here."

"Well," continued the Texan, "first, I would say women."

"We won't bother about that," said the Lord. "Go on, go on."

"Second, I would say tequila."

"Go on," insisted the Lord.

"Third, I would say 'La Cucaracha' and his native land."

"Good," said the Lord, "you may go now. St. Peter, get François, the French fiddler."

"*Bueno*, Señor," said St. Peter.

"François," said the Lord, "can you play 'La Cucaracha'?"

"*Mais oui, Monseigneur*," said the Frenchman.

Immediately he tuned his instrument.

"Come out here on the balcony where the angels can hear you," said Nuestro Señor. "I'm anxious to know if they like the piece."

"*Très bien, Monseigneur*," bowed François.

He put his instrument beneath his chin; and, after tightening his bow and getting a long breath, he began:

> "*La cucaracha, la cucaracha,*
> *Ya no puede navegar.*
> *Porque le faltan, porque le faltan*
> *Sus patitas de detrás.*"

Suddenly, away out in the crowd a hat went sailing into the air, and someone yelled, "*Viva México!*"

"There he is, St. Peter," said Nuestro Señor. "Get him."

And that is the true story, *amigo*, of the only Mexican who ever went to heaven. And you see why they kicked him out.

⤳ THE PARROT TALE-TELLER

A RICH MERCHANT AND A STUDENT, while drinking one day at an inn, began to quarrel. The student said that women were fickle, and the merchant contended that they were as trustworthy as men.

"My wife would never disobey me," said the merchant.

"Any man's wife will disobey," said the student.

The argument continued until bets were placed. The student, having no cash at hand, was to serve the merchant three years without salary in case he lost, but if he won he was to receive double the amount of a clerk's salary.

Pretending a fews days' trip away on business, the merchant, after having exacted a promise from his young wife that she would pray for him each morning at mass during his absence and after having ordered the servant woman to keep the doors closed and locked, packed his saddlebags and left.

Then the student, in accordance with the agreement they had reached, knocked at the door and asked to speak to the merchant's wife.

He was told that under no conditions were strangers to enter the house while the husband was away.

Immediately he went to a magician friend—a relative of the devil—and explained the affair from beginning to end, the result being that he was changed into a parrot. Now as a parrot he entered the merchant's home through a small opening near the door.

"Look!" said the young woman the next morning when she discovered him. "Behold what a beautiful pet!"

"It is time for mass now," said the old servant woman. "We must hurry."

"Don't go to mass," said the parrot. "Don't go to mass, and I will tell you a story."

"What kind of a story?" asked the young woman.

"I will tell you," said the parrot, "if you will promise to remain and listen to it."

Although the church bells were ringing and the old woman insisted upon going immediately to mass, the merchant's wife promised the parrot that she would stay and hear the story through.

"Once upon a time," said the parrot, "while the king and queen of Spain with their little daughter were traveling through a forest some distance from their palace, the princess lost her favorite doll. They had returned home before the toy was missed. Immediately after the loss was discovered, the little girl, without the permission of her father and mother, left the castle and wandered away into the woods.

"Before long she was lost. After wandering for a night and a day, she came to a city. The people took her to their king, who, seeing that she was very beautiful, concluded that surely she was a princess and so gave her a home within his palace. Soon she had become a favorite with the ruler and the object of jealousy and spite on the part of his relatives.

"One morning, tiring of her toys, the little princess asked the king if she might go to the gardens and play with the other girls of the place.

" 'No,' said the king, 'you are a princess and must live like a princess.'

" 'Ask,' said a girl who had stood near the door and heard the king's answer, 'ask in this order: "By the soul of your daughter, may I go play?" '

"The princess had not heard of a daughter and felt that the request in this form was a reference to herself. Also, she did not know that the king had forbidden any reference to his daughter.

" 'By the soul of your daughter, may I go play?' asked the princess.

"She was thrown into a dungeon and wandered through dark halls and passages until she came to a room where lay a beautiful girl asleep.

" 'Wake up, please, and tell me where I am,' said she, touching the sleeping girl's cheek.

" 'This girl is enchanted,' thought the princess. 'She is like the sleeping beauty of a story the nurse used to tell. I shall try the magic words of the story and see what happens.'

"The girl awoke and said she was the king's daughter, and

shortly the two of them found their way from the dungeon and had come before the king.

" 'My daughter!' said he. 'Is it really true? Can it be true that you have broken the enchanted sleep?'

" 'She is no longer asleep,' said the princess of Spain. 'The spell has been broken.'

"The king was overjoyed. 'I shall adopt you,' he said. 'You shall be my second daughter and shall inherit half my kingdom.'

" 'It was nothing to wake her,' said the princess. 'I need no reward, for I am the princess of Spain.'

" 'Why didn't you tell me before?' asked the king.

" 'Because,' said the princess, 'as you now see, the time for that had not arrived.'

"The princess of Spain returned to her parents, and a great celebration was declared at her homecoming.

"Now, *Mamacita*," concluded the parrot to the merchant's wife, "did you like the story?"

"Yes, indeed," said the latter.

The women did not attend mass that day, but spent the time making a perch for the parrot.

"It is time for mass," said the servant the following morning. "Hurry, señora, or else we shall be late."

The merchant's wife hurriedly dressed and was preparing to leave when the parrot called, "*Mamacita, mamacita,* I have a new story."

"New story! May God bless me, señora, we must go to mass," said the servant.

"No, *Mamacita*," cried the parrot. "There will be another mass, but after today there will never be a story like this."

"You know the promise you made your husband," continued the servant. "You promised to pray every day for his safe return."

"I can pray here," said the young woman. "I must hear the story. Go ahead, *periquito*, tell me the story."

"Well, once upon a time," said the parrot, "in the Land of Far Away there was a princess who had been afflicted with a strange disease. She could not talk, and, once she fell asleep, days would pass before she awoke again. The king, her father, called the wise men of his kingdom, and it was their opinion that the princess of

Spain should be requested to come to the bedside of their princess.

"A ship set sail and within a few weeks returned. The princess of Spain was aboard; and as soon as she reached the castle, she was taken to see the afflicted girl.

"'Lock us within this room tonight,' said the princess. 'I shall sleep in the same bed with your daughter, and tomorrow she will be cured.'

"At twelve o'clock that night a dim light entered the room. A Turk entered, took from beneath the bed a hidden key, and with it loosened the tongue of the girl afflicted. Then, while the princess of Spain pretended to sleep, the two talked at length. Their talk disclosed that the girl had refused to marry the Turk and that he in turn had brought a spell upon her so that she could speak only when her tongue was loosened with a magic key.

"It was a simple cure for the princess of Spain. When she made a sign of the cross, the Turk dropped his key and fled, and the sick princess was made well again.

"When the king offered half his kingdom in payment for the cure, the princess of Spain refused it, saying: 'It was nothing that I did. Thank the Virgin Mary.'

"*Mamacita*," concluded the parrot, "did you like the story?"

"Yes, indeed," she said.

The women did not go to church that day; instead they amused themselves talking to the parrot.

The following morning the servant called, "Up, señora, up; it is time for mass."

"*Mamacita*," called the parrot, "I have another story."

"Remember the promise to your husband," said the old servant. "You must go to mass and pray for his safe return."

"*Mamacita*," said the parrot, "stay and hear my story or I shall leave and never return."

"My husband won't know the difference," said the young woman. "I will stay."

"Once upon a time," said the parrot, "a prince in a land not far away was with a party hunting in the woods when by chance he found a doll. 'What a beautiful doll!' said he. 'I must meet the girl who owned it.'

"His men called to him and begged that he continue the hunt, but his only answer was, 'What a beautiful doll! I must meet the girl who owned it.'

"The chase was abandoned. The prince returned to the palace and lay down to rest.

" 'Are you tired?' asked the queen.

"The answer was, 'What a beautiful doll! I must meet the girl who owned it.'

"The prince was put to bed, ill with brain fever, and day and night he repeated, over and over again, 'What a beautiful doll! I must meet the girl who owned it.'

"The fame of the princess of Spain had reached the ears of the king of this foreign land, and he sent for her. Weeks passed, the ship returned, and the princess entered the palace. She was shown to the prince's room. Upon entering, the first thing she saw was the doll.

" 'My doll!' she cried. 'How strange!'

" 'Your doll?' asked the prince.

" 'Yes,' said the princess. 'I lost it in a forest seven years ago.'

" 'I am no longer ill,' said the prince, 'for I have found the girl who owns the doll.'

"The two were married. They became the king and queen of Spain and ruled that land for many years.

"*Mamacita*," said the parrot to the merchant's wife, "did you like the story?"

"Yes, indeed," she said, "but there is knocking at the door."

The door was opened, and as the husband entered the parrot disappeared.

"What is wrong?" asked the husband. "Aren't you happy that I am home again?"

"It isn't that," said the young wife. "My pet, a talking parrot, has this moment flown away and I feel that he will never return."

"Strange," mused the husband; "strange that you should regret the loss of a parrot at a time like this. How came the bird here?"

The wife told how it was found in the house the morning after the husband's departure, spoke of the stories, and in a forgetful moment in her narrative admitted that she had not gone to mass and had not prayed for the safe return of her husband. Realizing that he had lost the bet, the man gave way to his wrath and the two argued and quarreled all that day, the next, and the next, and some say they would be quarreling still if it weren't that the devil came and took them away.

∿ THE TWO COMPADRES

THESE WERE TWO COMPADRES. ONE was rich and the other poor. The rich man was very genial, and never a day passed that he didn't make it a point to greet his *compadre* and *comadre*. But further than an exchange of *buenos días* he gave nothing; and since his *compadre* was very poor, his niggardliness was resented.

"*Vieja*," said the poor man to his señora, "I've thought of a scheme. We must get money from our *compadre*. Go to the place where you grind *masa* and ask the family to lend us twenty cents; then buy a pen, ink, and paper. I shall go into the chaparral and catch two jackrabbits."

Within two hours rabbits, paper, ink, and pen were at hand.

"Now, old woman," the poor *compadre* said, "sit just outside the door, and call to me when you see our *compadre*."

Presently the señora said, "Here he comes."

The poor *compadre* seated himself quickly at the table and with pen in hand pretended to be very busy writing a letter.

"*Buenos días, comadre*," the rich man greeted the woman. "*Cómo le amaneció?* [How did you get up this morning?]"

"Very well, thanks, *compadre*. Only we have little to eat."

"And my *compadre*, where is he?" asked the rich man, ignoring the hint.

"*Ai 'ta dentro*," responded the *comadre*. "He is inside writing a letter to a friend in the city."

"*Buenos días, compadre*," the poor man greeted the rich man. "You will pardon the delay in speaking to you. I am in a hurry to get a letter off to a friend in the city."

"Then I will not detain you, since surely you will need to hurry to the post office."

"No, *señor compadre*," responded the poor man. "I don't mail my letters. I have a rabbit that is trained to run errands. He does the job quicker and saves me stamps."

Thereupon the poor *compadre* tied the letter to the rabbit's neck and turned him loose. The rich *compadre* was surprised at the speed with which the pet took off down the flat.

"When will he return from the city?" he asked.

"Not later than tomorrow," said the poor *compadre*. "You see how he runs. Neither hound nor hawk will stop him."

"Marvelous," said the rich man. "I shall return tomorrow to learn more about this wonderful rabbit. If he's as good as you say, I must buy him."

The following day the poor *compadre* said to his señora, "Look, *vieja*, sit just outside the door and call to me when you see our *compadre*."

She sat and presently said, "There comes our *compadre*."

Then the poor *compadre* brought in the other rabbit and ran him about the room until he was almost winded and was panting like a horse with the thumps.

"*Buenos días, comadre*," said the rich man as he entered. "Has my *compadre's* pet returned yet with the mail?"

"*Sí*, señor. Come in; it has just this instant arrived. Your *compadre* is reading the letter now."

"*Quiubo, compadre*," called the poor man. "*Pase, hombre*. Only look at this! Good time, don't you think?"

He handed the rich man a letter addressed to himself that he had just that morning faked.

"And look how winded my rabbit is! Once on the flat he travels like the wind."

"*Pues sí*," said the rich man, "it is all very good. However, you don't need him as I do. Sell him to me, *compadre*. How much will you take—one hundred dollars?"

"You know, *compadre*, I would sooner sell him to you than anyone else; yet it is impossible. First, he's a pet; and second, I need him."

"But I need him worse," said the rich man. "I will give you five hundred dollars for him."

"No, *compadre*, I am sorry, but . . ."

The rich *compadre* stooped quickly, picked up the rabbit, and said, "*Adiós, compadre*. I'm taking him with me. If you want a thousand dollars, come to my house."

The deal was made, and the rich *compadre* began writing letters.

His señora, too, wrote many letters. After a bit she said, *"Mira, hijo,* I must return these jewels to our friend in the city. Will our rabbit take them?"

"Cómo no?" said the man. "He's perfectly safe. He travels like the wind across the flat. Neither hound nor hawk will be able to stop him."

They made a package of the jewels and the letters and tied it to the rabbit's neck. He took off with a speed that amazed them both, and the man said, "You will see; tomorrow morning early he will be back with the answers."

However, the morrow came and went and so did the day following without the rabbit's returning. The third day a cruel suspicion dawned upon the rich *compadre*, and he swore to get revenge.

In the meantime the poor *compadre* had been busy cooking another pie for his friend.

"Vieja," he said to his wife, "take this peso to the market square and buy a beef's bladder and a quart of blood, and on the way home find some kind of rare flower. Bring these to me, and sit just outside the door and call to me when you see our *compadre."*

The flower, blood, and bladder were brought; and the man explained that the rich *compadre* would be very angry when he arrived and would likely want to fight.

"You," he said, "you put the bladder filled with blood beneath your blouse on the left side, and when we become noisy, come to me and say: 'Look, *viejo,* you mustn't quarrel with my *compadre.* You two will end by becoming angry.' Then I will jump to my feet and stab the bladder and say, 'Woman of the devil, attend to your own business.' Then you fall as if dead, and our *compadre* will feel compromised. I will then take the flower and pass it before your face. You must sit up. I will do this again and you will stand. And on the third pass of the flower you will smile and say, 'I feel well again.' "

All being arranged to the finest detail, the *comadre* sat just outside the door. Presently she said, *"A-a-a viene mi compadre."*

The man pretended to be busy.

"*Buenos días, comadre,*" said the rich man. "Is my *compadre* here? I must speak with him."

"*Pase, compadre,*" said the poor man.

The quarrel began immediately. One accused the other of fraud and the other denied the accusation.

"Look, *viejo,*" said the woman, "you mustn't quarrel with my *compadre.* You two will end by being angry."

Thereupon the poor man sprang to his feet and stabbed her. She fell to the floor, and the blood ran from the wound.

"*Dios mío!*" said the rich man. "What have you done, *compadre?* They will hang us for this."

"Don't worry," said the poor man. "I have a magic flower of life. Behold."

He took the flower from his pocket and with the first pass before the wounded woman's face she sat up, with the second she stood, and with the third she said she was well again.

"Sell me that flower," said the rich *compadre.*

"No, *compadre,* I can't; I expect to go to the city, and once there I shall get rich curing people of all kinds of ills."

"I will give you one thousand dollars for your magic flower."

"No, *compadre.* Something will go wrong, and then you will blame me."

"Blame you for what, *compadre?*" said the rich man.

He snatched the flower from the poor man and said, "If you want twenty-five thousand dollars, come to my house."

The bargain was made.

"I saw our *compadre* leaving here," said the rich man's wife upon returning from mass. "You must have nothing to do with him. Remember the rabbit."

"Remember nothing," said the rich man. "Listen, woman of the devil, attend to your own business."

Thereupon he stabbed her, and she fell to the floor.

The daughter and the servants began to weep.

"Shut up, you," said the man. "It is nothing. I have a magic flower of life. Behold, and you will see her come alive."

He passed the flower before the dead one's face, but she did not sit up. He repeated this and she did not stand. He repeated it once more and she did not speak. She was dead, *de veras.*

"*Ay, ay, ay,*" wailed the man. "So soon as I shall have buried my señora, I shall go immediately and kill my *compadre.*"

In the meantime the poor man was setting another trap for his *compadre.*

"*Vieja,*" he said, "get four candles and a large white cloth. Your *compadre* will be here soon, and I must play dead."

Candles and cloth were brought. The man laid himself flat on the floor and crossed his hands over his chest. The woman covered him with the sheet and put two lighted candles at the head and two at the feet. Then she sat just outside the door and presently said, "*A-a-a viene mi compadre.*" And the man lay as still as death.

"*Buenos días, comadre,*" said the rich man.

The woman began weeping bitterly and did not return the greeting.

"What is the matter, *comadre?*" said the rich man.

"Your—your—*compadre* is dead," said she.

The rich man removed his hat and entered the room.

"Too bad, *comadre.* What killed my *compadre?*"

"Too—too—toothache," wept the woman.

"Ha!" said the rich man. "Strange that he should die of toothache. Living or dead, however, I think I shall take him with me."

Thereupon he unfolded a large sack, and slipped it over the body of his *compadre* and tied it securely.

Just then he heard a burro passing by, and he called to the two *arrieros* driving it to help with the sack and its contents. They placed the load on the animal and made off *calle arriba* (up the street) for the rich man's home.

Upon arriving there he told the *arrieros* to wait until he saddled his horse. He entered his corral and left them at the gate.

"I wonder what is in this sack," whispered an *arriero.*

"*Ay, ay,*" came a voice from within, "take me down and I'll tell."

They removed the sack from the burro.

"*Ay, ay,*" came the voice, "untie the sack and I'll tell."

They untied the sack.

"*Ay, ay,*" said the man, "lift me to my feet and I'll tell."

They lifted him and he said, "My *compadre* is trying to compel me to marry a rich girl. Though I explained that I have a family, he wouldn't listen, and for that you see me here."

"I'm not married," said an *arriero*. "I will marry the rich girl for you, *con mucho gusto*."

They placed the *arriero* in the sack; and before the poor man escaped *calle abaja* (down the street), he had them promise to say nothing to the rich *compadre* about the change.

Presently the rich man returned, all booted and spurred and ready to ride.

"Where is your friend?" he asked the *arriero*.

"He had some business to attend to and asked me to stay and help you."

"Here are ten pesos," said the rich man. "I won't need you now. Leave the burro to me."

He drove to the sea, removed the load, and dumped it into the water. Then he returned to town and sat in front of his house to read a newspaper. Presently he saw seated against the wall just across the street another man.

"For the life of me," he said, "it is my *compadre. Oiga*, you, listen, *compadre*; come over here. How did you make out, *compadre*?"

"I'm provoked," said the poor man. "You dumped me into the sea but not far enough out. Look!"

When released from the sack at the corral gate, the poor *compadre* had gone home and thence to the thickets. While he was there, fate so had it that he found the jewels the rabbit had lost.

"Look at these pearls," said he. "The ocean bed is covered with them, and the people of the sea gave me these before I came away."

"What?" said the rich man. "I must have some jewels like that. *Compadre*, do me the favor to tie me in a sack and dump me into the ocean at the very place where you fell."

"No, *compadre*," said the poor man. "Something will go wrong and you will blame me."

"By no means, friend. Look, I will put my hacienda in trust for you. Do me this one great favor, *compadre*."

"Very well," said the poor man.

The trust was made; the rich *compadre* was duly sacked and dumped into the sea in accordance with his own wishes, and the poor *compadre* is now rich. He is held in great esteem by the people of his town for many innocent little pranks.

◟ THE FAITHFUL LION

ONCE A HUNTER CAPTURED A LION
cub and gave it as a pet to his only daughter. With foreboding and
regret the father watched the rapid growth of the beast.

"Take care," said a neighbor, "lest some day he yield to his
inborn instincts. It is dangerous to allow your daughter to feed and
caress him."

"Henriqueta," said the father, "our neighbor is right. We must
destroy your pet."

"No, father," said the girl, "he must not be killed."

The father yielded on condition that the animal be chained to
a tree. Sometime thereafter Henriqueta began to meet secretly near
a *laguna* one of several lovers. Four bandits learned of this, and it
was agreed among them to wait for her in ambush near the trysting
place and kidnap her for ransom.

So it happened one evening while the father was away that
they captured the girl, gagged her, tied her hands and feet, and
placed her on a horse ridden by the leader. Then all rode at break-
neck speed for their camp in the mountains.

Each time upon her return from the *laguna*, it was Henriqueta's
custom to stop at the large tree at the rear of the house and pet
the lion. On this occasion when she did not return to the tree, the
lion grew restless. He would walk to and fro, lie down, yawn, and
with head lifted high look down the dark path toward the *laguna*.
Then he would whine and resume his restless yawning and pacing
to and fro. At last either the suspense or a premonition of danger
so aroused him that he screamed and sprang and ran on his chain
with such fury that the collar broke; then a large shadow slipped
through the brush to the banks of the *laguna*. There was a brief
pause and the animal disappeared.

The bandits had gone some five leagues when their horses began
to show signs of fear. It was only with much quirting and spurring
that they were kept on the *sendero* (path).

The cause for alarm apparently vanished. Then, while the
bandits were trailing along the banks of a ravine beneath large,
overhanging trees, the lion dropped from a limb upon the neck
of the horse carrying the girl. Mount and riders were thrown to

the ground. The bandit leader was killed, and with great haste the others took to their heels.

When Henriqueta's father returned to the ranch, he missed his daughter and ran to the large tree. The missing lion, to him, meant only one thing. Henriqueta had been slain and carried away.

He called his men, armed them, and began a hunt that lasted into the following day. At last, with all hopes gone, they returned home. There they found Henriqueta lying exhausted on the porch, and to their amazement there was the lion nearby, watching over her.

Chapter Three

⌐ TRUTHFUL JOHN

El pan para los muchachos,   Bread for children,
El salvado para los machos,   Bran for mules,
Y el vino para los borrachos.   And wine for drunkards.

IN A CERTAIN GRANJA THERE WAS A cowherd whose name was Juan. Since he never lied, he was called Juan Verdadero. Afternoons when he returned from the fields with the stock, one would hear the following conversation between him and the *patrón:*

"Juan Verdadero, how is the herd?"

"Some fat, some poor, upon my word."

"And the white and greenish-colored bull?"

"Señor, quite green and beautiful."

One day the owner of the adjoining farm visited Juan's *patrón.*

"Our neighbor," said he, "is a great liar. He tells me he received forty pesos a head for his cows. What a liar! Doesn't it seem that way to you?"

"But, *compadre,*" said the *patrón,* "it may be true."

"No," said the neighbor, "any man under the urge of necessity will lie."

"Not true," said the *patrón*; I have a *vaquero* on the place who never lies."

"So I have heard. I will bet you my *granja* against your *granja* that your boy Juan Verdadero can be induced to lie," said the neighbor.

"I'll bet he can't," said the *patrón*.

Next day the neighbor sent his beautiful daughter with a diamond ring to the fields in search of Juan Verdadero. She found him, placed the ring in his hand, and asked, "Juan, do you like this ring?"

Juan, who had never before seen a thing so valuable, was quite carried away.

"I shall present it to you," said the girl, "if in return you will give me the heart of the green bull."

"No," said Juan, "for then what should I tell the *patrón*?"

"Oh, you can tell him a wild beast ate the bull. . . . You are honest; the *patrón* will believe you."

Juan struggled with himself, but the desire to possess the ring overcame him.

The bull was killed and its heart was given to the girl, who, overjoyed, departed immediately for her *granja*.

Now Juan had never lied before, and he found it hard to invent a credible falsehood. No sooner would he choose a story than it seemed unbelievable. He removed his coat, hung it on a post, and placing his hat atop, kneeled before it as if it were the *patrón*. Then he said:

"Juan Verdadero, how is the herd?"

"Some fat, some poor, upon my word."

"And the white and greenish-colored bull?"

Here he paused. Three times he repeated this without finding it possible to lie.

The evening shadows lengthened toward the east, and the diamond lost its luster. Juan, now weeping in despair, must return with his cows to the ranch house and, without the green bull, must face the *patrón*.

The two men waited at the corral gate. The neighbor smiled with condescending patience as the *patrón* began:

"Juan Verdadero, how is the herd?"

"Some fat, some poor, upon my word."

"And the white and greenish-colored bull?"

There was no answer.

Again the *patrón* repeated:

"Juan Verdadero, how is the herd?"

"Some fat, some poor, upon my word."

"And the white and greenish-colored bull?"

"Dead, señor, dead."

"What?" shouted the *patrón*, pretending anger.

Juan, kneeling before him, hold how a girl as pretty as the summer's dawn had given him a diamond ring for the heart of the bull, and how, in a moment of weakness, he had yielded.

The *patrón* was overjoyed.

"Juan Verdadero," he said, "from now on you are the *administrador* of my *granja*."

The neighbor was compelled to give over his entire estate, for he had lost the bet.

¿Quieres que te lo cuente otra vez?	Shall I tell it to you again?
Éste era un gato,	This was a cat,
Con los pies de trapo,	With feet of tatters
Y los ojos al revés.	And eyes turned back.

⤺ CHARGE THIS TO THE CAP

THESE WERE TWO COMPADRES. ONE was rich and the other poor. "*Vieja*," said the latter to his wife one day, "it isn't right that we should starve. I'm going to ask our rich *compadre* to help us."

Upon reaching the rich man's house, the poor *compadre* was received badly. He asked for food but received not so much as sympathy. In fact, the rich *compadre* was discourteous to the extent of laughing at the poor man, at his attitude and clothing, and at his hat in particular.

"You need no help, *compadre*," said he. "Go sell your cap. As a curiosity it is worth a fortune; and it is so full of holes, it is at least a good riddle to set people guessing just when it will decide to be no cap at all."

Three years passed and the poor *compadre*'s luck, which could not have been worse, was now somewhat better.

"*Vieja*," said he, "I'm going to take the little money we have and get even with our rich *compadre*."

First he bought himself a gray cap with a blue band; then he went to a watchmaker's shop and bought a cheap watch.

"*Amigo*," he said to the watchmaker, "I need your help. My *compadre*, a very rich man, has insulted me, and you can help me get revenge. After we have changed the price tag to indicate a very valuable timepiece, I shall leave the watch with you and call for it later. When I return you are to act as if you have never seen me before; and I shall pretend to be buying the watch for the first time. I shall take it, point to my gray cap, and say, '*Debo de gorra* [charge this to the cap]'; and you are to respond, 'You owe me nothing; take it.'"

Being assured of the watchmaker's help, the poor *compadre* went to a jeweler, bought a string of imitation pearls, and made the same arrangements with him that he had made with the watchmaker. "When I take the pearls and say, '*Debo de gorra*,' you are to say, 'You owe me nothing; take them.'"

From the jewelry store our poor *compadre* went next to a dry goods store and bought a suit, and then to an inn, where he paid for two meals. In each case it was understood that on his return he was to point to his gray cap and say, "*Debo de gorra*," instead of paying for his purchase.

With the trap well set, he visited his rich *compadre* and, being well dressed, was received with excessive courtesy.

"*Compadre*," said the rich man, "what a fine new cap! What kind is it?"

"Oh, it isn't so much," said the poor man; "yet it has proved valuable upon more than one occasion. However, *compadre*, I've come to town to make some purchases. If you don't mind, I should be pleased to have you accompany me. After this business is attended to, you shall be my guest at dinner."

"*Con mucho gusto*," said the rich *compadre*, who was much in favor of getting something for nothing. "It will be a great pleasure to accept your invitation."

They went first to the watchmaker's shop.

"Let me see a good watch," said the poor man.

"A good watch will cost a lot of money," said the merchant.

"It isn't the price; it's the watch that counts," said the customer. "I'll take that one marked three hundred dollars."

The watch was handed to the poor *compadre*.

"*Debo de gorra*," said he, pointing to his gray cap.

"You owe me nothing; take it," said the merchant.

The rich *compadre* was amazed but held his peace.

The two went immediately to the jewelry store. Here the imitation pearls had been marked up to one thousand dollars. The poor *compadre* took them and said, "*Debo de gorra*."

"You owe me nothing; take them," said the jeweler.

Next they entered the dry goods store, and the suit was bought and paid for with a point to the cap and the words, "*Debo de gorra*."

The two *compadres* went to an inn and had dinner, and to all appearances this too, like the suit, pearls, and watch, was paid for with a salute to the gray hat and the words, "*Debo de gorra*."

"What a marvelous cap!" said the rich *compadre*. "Sell it to me."

"No, *compadre*," said the poor man. "I could hardly live without my gray cap with the blue ribbon."

"I will give you thirty thousand dollars for it," said the rich man.

After a bit of hesitancy on the part of the poor man, the deal was closed, and the rich *compadre* rushed home to tell his wife.

"*Hija*," said he, "this is to be the day of days. Come, we will buy whatever you want."

"How?" exclaimed the wife. "You will buy the diamond necklace I asked for a year ago?"

"Certainly, woman," boasted the rich man, "and even more."

They went to the best jewelry store in town and bought a diamond necklace. Then instead of paying for it the rich *compadre* pointed to his gray cap and said, "*Debo de gorra*."

"What does that mean?" asked the clerk.

"It means, stupid, that I don't have to pay for the necklace."

Evidently the clerk thought otherwise, for he had the rich *compadre* arrested.

Today the poor *compadre* lives in luxury, while the rich *compadre* is in a madhouse.

"It worked," says the rich *compadre* over and over again. "It worked; I saw it with my eyes. It is a magic cap, I tell you. The one who wears it never pays for a thing; all one needs to say is, '*Debo de gorra.*' "

⌐ TREASON IN SAINTS

IN AN INDIAN RANCHERÍA AT THE FOOT of a *sierra* lived two *compadres*, Juan and Tomás.

Juan was gentle and kind, and by the sweat of his brow earned an honest living, while Tomás, on the other hand, was lazy and lived by his wits.

Compa' Juan had been plowing his field in preparation for the planting of corn and beans. One morning upon entering the corral he found that one of his oxen was gone. He stood for a moment thinking, and then he said: "Perhaps it is my *compa'* Tomás; perhaps it is he who stole the ox. I will go to his house and look for evidence."

Before reaching the home of his *compadre*, he met the latter's little son.

"Good morning, *hijito*," he said. "Where is your *tata*?"

"At home," replied the child. "He has killed an ox and is stripping the flesh dry. The hide is up there under the cliffs."

Juan was calm.

"That is good," he said. "That is indeed very good, *hijito*. Maybe your *tata* will divide the meat with me."

Upon reaching the house, Juan greeted both his *compadre* and *comadre* and said, "*Compa'* Tomás, I have come to ask permission to consult your San Antonio. I am in trouble and need a revelation; and since your saint is so famous for his miracles, I feel he may help me."

"Yes, of course," said Tomás. "Why not? It will be a pleasure to lend you my San Antonio."

Thereupon he took a statuette from a shelf and handed it to Juan. It was Saint Anthony holding the child Jesus. Juan walked to one side and pretended to converse with the image. At last he crossed himself, placed the saint back on the shelf, and turned to Tomás.

"*Compa'* Tomás," he said abruptly, "be it known that last night an ox was stolen from my corral. Your San Antonio here says that you are the thief and that you are stripping the flesh to dry and have hid the hide under the cliffs. Now, since I was planning to kill that very ox and since you have so kindly done the work for me, I will say nothing to the authorities about the matter, on condition, of course, that you produce both meat and hide immediately."

Reluctantly Tomás admitted his guilt, brought forth the meat and hide, and sacked them for his neighbor. The latter, with many thanks, bade his *compadre* good day and disappeared down the trail.

Helpless, Tomás watched the reward of his cunning slip from his grasp. As he stared down the trail, his face became gradually that of a demon. He walked across the room to the little shelf, and with the very first blow of his machete, he knocked Saint Anthony from his place. The child Jesus, unharmed, rolled beneath the feet of the woman.

"Baby, no; baby, no," she begged, trying to save the little image from her husband's rage. "*Nene*, no; *nene*, no!"

"And why not? *Nene*, too, I tell you; *nene*, too, lest he grow up and become a traitor like his *tata*."

And thus it was that San Antonio and the Niño Jesus were destroyed for knowing and saying too much.

⌐ BALDHEADS

A FELLOW SENT HIS SON TO TOWN TO purchase food. Wishing to walk the streets a while and yet fearing to go about with money on his person, the youth decided to deposit his purse somewhere for safekeeping. He entered a house bearing the sign *Casa de Encargos*.

"Yes, *joven*," said a clerk, "you may, with all confidence, leave your money with us."

After four hours of sight-seeing, the youth was back for his money.

"What? Who are you? You deposited nothing here," said the clerk.

It was evident that this was not a bank but a place where country folk were skinned.

The youth returned home and told his father what had happened.

The father asked, "Can you describe the man who took your deposit?"

"Señor," said the son, "he was a bald-headed man."

"Not so good," said the father, "not so good."

"Tell me, son," continued the father, "is he balder than I?"

"No," responded the son, "not so bald by far."

"Then don't worry; just leave him to me. Come, let's go to town."

The father provided himself with a small buckskin bag. This he filled with buttons and rusty washers. Having told his son what to do, he entered the house bearing the sign *Casa de Encargos* and placed the bag on the counter.

He asked the clerk, "Señor, is this a bank? I should like to deposit some money here."

"Sí, señor," answered the clerk, "you may, with all confidence, leave your money with us."

At this moment, as prearranged, the son entered and asked the clerk for his money. The latter, fearing to lose a larger sum, said, "Yes, *joven*; here is your money."

After counting it out to him peso for peso, the clerk turned to the man and said, "This boy, señor, is my regular customer."

"I am glad to know that," said the father. "I wanted to be sure my son had left his money with you. You won't need this bag of buttons and rusty washers. *Con su permiso*, señor, I shall not deposit it. With your permission."

And, bowing politely, he left.

"Always keep an eye on baldheads, son," said the father.

⤙ JUAN PELÓN

THIS WAS A HARDHEADED BOY. ONCE his mother left the baby in his care. Juan Pelón, curious to know how children were put together, cracked his little brother's skull and took out his brains. When the mother returned, Juan said, "Look! The baby's head was full of worms."

On another occasion the mother left him at the house while she went for water. Juan Pelón made a nest, put eggs in it, and sat on them. When the mother returned, she found the door locked.

"*Ábreme la puerta*, Juan," she called.

"I can't open the door," answered Juan. "*Estoy cuelco* (I am setting)."

The mother called a priest, who, after much argument with the boy, convinced him that it was a hen's business to set.

At the mother's request the *padrecito* took Juan Pelón away in order to cure him of his absurd tricks.

Some days later the priest said to Juan, "Go buy a sack of grapes."

The boy bought the grapes and on his way back to the priest ate more than half of them. He emptied the remainder on the ground, filled the bottom of the sack with prickly pear leaves, and placed the grapes on top of them. He gave the sack to the priest who, without offering any of the fruit to Juan, began to eat, and each time he put his hand into the sack for a grape he said, "Ay, Juan Pelón."

"*Hay*,"[1] said Juan. "Yes, Little Father, *hay muchas* (there are many), but on top no; down below *hay*."

The priest plunged deep into the sack and got his hand full of thorns.

"*Ay, ay, ay!*" he shouted. "*Ay, Dios mío!*"

"Didn't I tell you, *padrecito?*" laughed Juan. "Of a truth *hay*."

The boy's sharp wit was repaid with a flogging.

Later the priest put eggs on the fire to boil and told Juan to sit near the door and watch them. The *padrecito* walked back and forth before the door, let wind each time he passed Juan Pelón, and said, "Eat *ese huevo*, Pelón."

Presently Juan went into the house and ate all the eggs.

The priest, at last having acquired a good appetite, entered, found the eggs gone, and asked, "Where are the eggs, Juanito?"

"I ate them," said the boy. "Didn't you tell me to eat the eggs?"

Juan Pelón was flogged again.

The priest lay down to rest; and when he had gone to sleep,

---

[1] The joke here is developed on a play of words. *Ay* and *hay* are pronounced alike; *ay* is an exclamation; *hay* means either *there is* or *there are*.

Juan stole two *talegas*[2] of money and hit for a *resaca* in the desert. He hung the coins on a tree in a way to suggest that they had grown there. Two mule drivers came along and bought the tree for four *talegas* of money.

Juan Pelón stole a ride on a wagon to the city. The law there was strict and *coyoteando*[3] was forbidden. He was arrested and placed in the *chirona*. No one was ever known to leave that particular prison alive. All the first night Juan heard the voices of two dead men.

"*Caigo ó no caigo?*" each kept saying. "Do I fall or do I not fall? Do I fall or do I not fall?"

"Why can't they fall?" thought Juan to himself.

"Buried in one corner of the jail is a jar of money," said one of the dead men, "and in the opposite corner is another. One is for you and one is for the poor."

Juan dug both jars of money up and awaited the coming of the executioner. Soon a jailer entered the door, and Juan killed him. Then came the executioner, and Juan killed him. The priest followed the executioner, and Juan killed him.

Juan Pelón left the jail and since then has not been seen.

[2] *Talega*, a bag of 1,000 dollars or pesos.
[3] Swiping, pickpocketing. A number of uncomplimentary slang words in use in Mexico are derived from *coyote*.

Chapter Four

⤳ PEDRO DE URDEMALAS

PEDRO DE URDEMALAS LIVES BY HIS
wits. In a way he is a liar but, different from Don Cacahuate, Tío
Aurelio, and Compadre Doroteo, he does not lie for the glory of
lying. His *mentiras* are a means to an end, and the most desirable
end to him is to skin the fellow who is out to get the other man's
side. However, he often tricks the innocently gullible. Also, being
a man of chance, he is a plaything of fate; one day he is rich and
the next poor.

Once, when considerably the worse for his manner of living
and while wandering along a highway tired, hungry, and without
money, he came to a hog ranch. It was the first of its kind he had
ever seen, and, despite his low spirits, he was greatly amused by
the great array of swine tails.

"There are many tails," said he, "and wherever there is a tail
there is a hog. This gives me an idea, and if it works I shall have
money to spend."

He took his knife and cut the tails from the hogs, and continued
on his way until he came to a *resaca*, or swamp. There he busied
himself sticking the hog-end of the tail stumps in the mud. Then,

after tramping around and digging up the earth about each, he sat beneath a willow and began to weep.

Presently a man rode up on horseback.

"Why are you weeping?" he asked.

Pedro wept louder than ever and said, "Why shouldn't I weep? I have lost a fortune in this bog hole. Those tails you see are all that is left to show for hogs that were."

"Poor fellow," said the stranger, "weep no more. I shall buy your herd and have my servants come and dig them out of this *atascadero*. How much do you want for them?"

"Señor," said Pedro de Urdemalas, "it is not my wish to sell them, for my life is wrapped up in these hogs. But you see how hopeless things are. Rather than lose them, I will sell them to you for one thousand dollars."

The trade was made. Pedro went away weeping until he was out of sight and then took to his heels.

The stranger brought his servants, and he wasn't long finding out how well he had been swindled. Frantic, he directed a search for Pedro but all to no avail. He gave up the hunt and did the only thing left for him to do, and that was to swear revenge in case he should ever again meet Pedro de Urdemalas.

Well, sir, true to form, there came a day when again Pedro was broke and hungry. Immediately he began devising a new lie with which to snare some sucker.

"I need twenty cents worth of *frijoles*, a pot, an underground furnace, and a little time," said he to himself.

He bought beans and pot, dug a furnace, and, after having burned some wood to coals, he put the pot over them and hid all traces of the fire. Presently the pot began to boil, and Pedro, with a long thorn, speared those *frijoles* that boiled to the top and ate them. He was amusing himself in this manner when a traveler approached.

"*Buenas tardes, buen amigo* (good-afternoon, good friend)," he said. "What are you doing?"

"No, nothing," said Pedro de Urdemalas, "just waiting for those who are to arise and enjoying those who go."

"Pardon," said the traveler, pointing at the pot, "what makes that thing boil?"

"Nothing; it is a magic pot," Pedro informed him. "In the preparation of my meals I never have to bother with fire. As soon as the food is in the pot and it is placed on the ground, it begins to boil."

Now, the stranger was a traveling man and figured that he needed just such a pot.

"How much do you want for it?" he asked.

"I don't care to sell it," said Pedro.

"I will give you a thousand dollars," bartered the traveler.

"See here, *amigo*," said Pedro de Urdemalas, "I am badly in need of money; otherwise I would not think of disposing of such a rare pot. It is a bargain, but we will have to take care lest it discover the change in masters and refuse to boil. Sit down very quietly and give me the money. Don't speak or move until I am out of hearing."

It was with the utmost caution that the trade was made. The stranger, almost afraid to breathe, sat by the boiling pot, and Pedro tiptoed away. After an hour of patient watching, the new owner of the magic vessel noticed that the beans and water were not boiling. He picked up the pot and immediately realized that he had been skinned. At first he swore revenge, but after second thought he was so humiliated by his gullibility that he was glad to forget about it.

It was late in the afternoon when Pedro de Urdemalas decided it would be safe to rest his weary legs. Tired out by the haste with which he left his last victim, he sat beneath a mesquite not far from the road and wondered how he might add another thousand dollars to his ill-gotten gain. Presently, he began boring holes in the coin he carried, and, when this was done, he hung it to the branches of the tree in such a manner that it appeared to have grown there.

The following morning two wagon masters on their way up the road were amazed by what they saw. They went to the mesquite and were about to pluck the rare fruit when Pedro saw them.

"*Eit, eit!*" he shouted. "Leave my tree alone."

They asked the name of the tree.

"This is the only one in existence," said Pedro de Urdemalas. "It bears twice a year, and it is time to gather this season's crop."

"How much do you want for this plant?" they asked.

"Don't insult me," said Pedro. "Why should I want to sell a tree like this? It would be foolish."

"We can pay your price," they insisted. "Besides, it isn't our intention to leave here before you agree to sell."

"Oh, well," said Pedro, "give me a thousand dollars and the present crop and the bargain is closed."

They agreed. Pedro gathered the coins from the tree, collected the purchase money, and left for parts unknown.

The wagon masters built homes near the mesquite, pruned it, watered it, and did all in their power to aid in a rich crop of coins the following season.

It being only a mesquite, their reward was mesquite beans.

These poor fools, like the others, had been beaten, but were thankful to have come off no worse.

Pedro, in the meantime, was, as an old *corrido* says, *"siempre caminando,"* always traveling.

One day, however, much to his surprise and great concern, he met a giant.

"Ay, Chihuahua!" said he, "this is an ugly business. How am I to manage now?"

Quickly, before the giant had seen him, he took a *guarache* from his foot and threw it into the air.

"What do you say?" said the giant. "If you feel strong, let's see if you can whip me."

Just then the *guarache* fell.

"What's this?" asked the giant.

Then Pedro de Urdemalas explained that three days earlier he had thrown a man into the air and this *guarache* was the first he had seen of him since.

The giant was frightened and figured that if that were the case it might be advisable to go easy with Pedro. However, gathering new courage, he said, "I'll bet you my life against yours you can't beat me at three stunts I know."

"What do you mean?" asked Pedro.

"First," said the giant, "let's see you ram your arm through the heart of this tree."

Pedro asked that he be given a day to prepare for the feat, and the giant agreed to the request and went away.

Pedro de Urdemalas thought for a long time. Then carefully he removed the bark from a large tree; after hollowing out a place in the trunk the size of his fist and the length of his arm, he placed its bark back again.

The next day the giant returned and asked if Pedro was ready to attempt the first feat. Upon being assured that he was, the giant said, "Choose your tree."

"I'll take this one," said Pedro, "and, since I accepted the challenge, I'll hit first."

He walked to the tree and with an easy jab sent his fist an arm's length into the trunk.

The giant admitted he was beaten and chose not to hit.

"The second feat," said he, "is to see who can throw a stone the farther."

Having been granted a day for preparation and the giant having gone away, Pedro de Urdemalas caught a quail, and on the following morning hid it beneath his blouse.

The giant returned, chose to throw first, and sent a stone a quarter of a league before it came to earth.

"Stand away," said Pedro. "I must wind up."

And while the giant was not looking, Pedro pretended to throw and turned the quail loose.

"There it goes," said he.

The bird passed out of sight while still rising into the air. The giant admitted that Pedro's stone had gone the farther.

"Tomorrow we will wrestle," he said.

Pedro de Urdemalas spent the night tearing up the soil and breaking down the chaparral. He tore his clothes and scratched his hands.

The next morning, when the giant asked the meaning of the strange disorder, Pedro replied, "No, nothing; I've been fighting a man larger than you."

"Where is he?" asked the giant.

"I threw him into the air and he hasn't come down yet," said Pedro.

"*Caray!*" said the giant. "I'm glad to admit you are the better man. However, before you take my life, come be my guest tonight in my home."

In the guest's room immediately above the bed there hung by
a trigger a large iron bar released by a rope back of the door. After
supper Pedro de Urdemalas was shown to bed. But not for nothing
had Pedro lived by his wits, and before long he discovered the
trap. He arranged the covers so as to suggest a body beneath them
and hid behind the door.

At midnight the giant quietly entered the room and crept to
the bedside to see just how the sleeper lay. When he leaned over
the bed, Pedro released the iron bar and the giant was killed.

Pedro left this place. Three days later, while walking along the
road, he came face to face with the man who had bought the swine
tails from him.

"Now you are going to pay," said the man, catching Pedro by
the arm. "You have had a lot of fun during your life, but now that
is all over."

"It is all very true," said Pedro. "Dispose of me whenever you
please."

Pedro de Urdemalas was taken to the hacienda and there was
placed in a large barrel. The lid was fastened on the barrel, and
one little hole was bored in the side.

"We will eat dinner," said the man to the servants, "and then
we will take him to the river and drown him."

Pedro remained quiet until they were out of hearing and then
began rocking the barrel. This had been left near a slope; and
when it turned over, it began rolling away from the house and
came to a halt in a meadow near a herd of sheep.

"*Buen amigo, buen amigo!*" called Pedro.

A herder came to the barrel and asked, "What's the matter?"

"Nothing at all except that they are trying to compel me to
marry the king's only daughter," said Pedro. "If you care to, you
may take my place."

"*De veras?*" asked the herder.

"Yes," said Pedro, "it's true; only get me out of here and you
get in."

The change was made and the barrel was rolled back to the
top of the slope and placed where the man and his servants had
left it. Then Pedro gathered the sheep and drove them away.

In due time the barrel and contents were thrown into the river, and, as the barrel sank from sight, there came the gurgling sound of *gori-gori-gori-gori, glu, glu, glu.*

Some days later the man and his servants were hunting.

"Isn't that the man we drowned?" asked one of them, pointing to a herder some distance away.

"I'll swear it is," said the man.

They approached and spoke to Pedro de Urdemalas.

"I thought you were drowned," said the man.

"Didn't you hear the *gori-gori-gori* when the barrel sank?" asked Pedro. "Well, each *gori* was a sheep. Once the barrel was on the river bottom, the underwater people opened it and let me go."

"What shall we do with him, boys?" said the man.

"He's had enough," said the servants. "Let him go."

Pedro de Urdemalas sold his sheep and entered the king's service. The ruler was a great tease and made life miserable for his servants. However, Pedro turned the trick on him so often the king was offended.

"Take this rascal and hang him," said he.

"Grant me a last request," pleaded Pedro.

"Very well," said the king.

"Let me choose the tree upon which I'm to be hanged."

"Granted," said the king. "Soldiers, go hang him and never let me see his face or hear of him again."

Pedro de Urdemalas chose to be hanged from a sunflower plant. The soldiers were perplexed. They had heard the last wish granted, and also they were afraid to bring the matter again to the king's attention. Consequently, they released Pedro de Urdemalas on condition that he never show his face again.

⌐, KEEPING THE SHIRTTAIL IN

TWO MEN, FAMOUS IN THE ART OF lying, met one day at the crossroads.

"Where have you been, *amigo*?" asked one.

"*Amigo*," responded the other, "I've been afar and have seen miracles and wonders."

"Yes?" responded the first. "Listen to me if you should care to learn about miracles and wonders. Just listen to me."

"Very well, what have you to say?" asked the first.

"Well, for instance, I saw a pumpkin that was so large a shepherd used its hollow in which to bed a thousand sheep at night."

"Wait," interrupted the first; "that reminds me. I, while traveling through Italy, saw an oven so large it took a thousand men to fire it."

"Why," gasped the other, "why such large ovens?"

"To cook your pumpkins in," answered the friend.

"You are good, *amigo*," said the victim. "In fact, if truth weren't distasteful to me I'd swear you were my master. Let's combine our virtues and earn our living lying. You tell 'em and I'll swear to 'em. Yet I warn you, if your exaggerations get top-heavy, I may find it hard to cooperate. Let's say in such a case I give your shirttail a jerk. That will be the sign to cut down a bit."

Having reached an agreement in all matters pertaining to their procedure, they continued on their way. Presently they came to a town and approached a group of men on the plaza.

"In my country," began the master, "rattlesnakes are a mile long."

His companion, fearing such audacity, jerked the other gently by the shirttail.

"They may not be a mile long at that," retracted the first, "but they are easily a half-mile in length."

The modest companion continued to tug at the shirttail.

"Of course, they could be shorter, but I'd swear that if their shirttails were out, they would be two yards long."

The people could stand no more.

"Kill the cowards," they cried. "Run them out of town."

"You see," said the master as he looked back upon the place, "people prefer lies straight. A diluted lie is a sin against art. Follow my advice: keep your own shirttail in and leave mine alone."

They chose to travel separately. The master was to lead and the friend was to follow.

Presently the first man entered a wretched little village. He told the people that in the last town he had passed through there was a newborn baby with seven heads. This news caused much interest, and the informant was given all the food he could eat.

Presently the next man arrived.

"Señor," the people asked, "is it true that in a town up the way a child was born with seven heads?"

"Why, señores," gasped the late arrival, "I . . . I couldn't exactly swear to that, but . . . but . . ."—he stuck his shirttail in and continued—"but on a *mecate* [a rope line] I saw hanging out to dry a little shirt with seven collars on it."

This fellow, too, like the first, was treated with much consideration.

These liars are still lying, and you may be sure they both keep their shirttails in.

WINE AND THE DEVIL

THE WORLD HAD BEEN MADE AND GOD was preparing to plant the vineyard when the devil asked, "What are you doing?"

"I'm planting some grapes," said God. "There will be times in the life of man when he will need wine to cheer him up."

"Would you mind if I help?" asked the devil.

God meditated for a bit. "What is he up to now?" thought he. At last, feeling no harm could be done, he said, "All right, you may help."

"You will be surprised at my efficiency," said the devil.

He went to work immediately. First, he killed a mockingbird and sprinkled the blood along the rows. Then he killed a lion and then a swine and sprinkled their blood, too, from one end of the vineyard to the other.

"A' 'stá listo," said he. "Now we are ready, and we shall see what happens."

We are all well aware what happens. When a man first begins drinking he feels the effects of the bird's blood and sings. He continues to drink until fired by the lion's blood; then he fights. His thirst increases until he has drunk as deep as the swine's blood, and the next thing we know he is in the gutter.

Ay, que mala suerte! What ill fate!

↜ EL BORRACHO DEL BAHIO

CHANO CALANCHE WAS A BORRACHO. He was seldom sober, for there was nothing he disliked more than to look upon this cold and prosaic world through eyes uninspired by liquor. *Por eso*, señor, he was drunk most of the time. However, now and then, lacking the *conqué* (wherewithal) to purchase drinks —for be it known, señor, that Chano Calanche, like myself, was miserably poor—and fearing sobriety as if it were a plague, he begged, borrowed, stole, and even worked for his mescal.

Upon this occasion, being broke and nearly sober and having been followed by bad luck from one cantina to another, he had decided to try the only chance left him, the Cantina del Aguililla, which was located near the outskirts of the *villa*.

It was a dark and stormy night. Bandits, after having murdered three priests, had made themselves at home at the Cantina del Aguililla. The bodies of two of the unfortunates had been dragged back of the bar, and the third lay near a table around which the outlaws sat when Calanche entered.

"*Buenas noches, caballeros*," said he. "Is there one of you who would favor me with a drink?"

"Who are you?" asked the bandit captain.

"I am," responded Chano, "the most miserable man in the world. Some are born happy, that is to say, in the good graces of God; some sing and are happy; but I, *caballeros*, am happy only when I have taken a little, and just now I am suffering the torments of being broke and dry."

"Ah," said the captain, who had quickly guessed Chano's financial rating, "so my good man would be tight and happy and yet hasn't the price of a drink. I know of only one solution to your problem, *amigo*: earn your happiness; whether by the point of a pistol or by labor, earn it. Here," continued the captain, "is a dead *padrecito* who should not be found in this disreputable place. If you will take him to the thickets and lose him, I will see to it that you are given the finest quart of wine in this cantina."

Chano had not seen the corpse near the table. But now, with the prospects of good cheer so near at hand, he could hardly be expected to bother about the whys and wherefores of a dead priest.

"That is a bargain," said he, "only that you give me one little glass of mescal to start me off."

The mescal was poured for him. Then, with the corpse over his shoulder, the drunkard left the *villa* by way of a small trail. Upon reaching the chaparral, he made straight for a mining shaft and with little feeling and formality threw the corpse into the abandoned hole.

In the meantime the outlaws had thought up a good prank. Betting on the drunkard as an easy mark, they dragged one of the two corpses from behind the bar and laid it near the table in the very same position occupied by the one just carried away.

"Here I am back," announced Chano upon reentering the saloon. "*Mi capitán*, I did as you commanded; I lost the *padrecito*."

The captain, laughing like a demon, coughed and choked with laughter. "What do you say to that, boys?" said he. "A curious sense of the ridiculous, no? Our friend leaves the room, but the *padrecito* does not go with him. Perhaps we were to send the *padrecito* to you, *amigo*, and so? *Bueno*, it's our fault. But now, see here," he said, "pick up this priest, hold him tight, and don't let him go until you have lost him in the thickets. You understand?"

Chano was too confused for understanding. "Señores," he said, hesitating to touch the corpse that lay at his feet. "Señores, am I dreaming? I've had weird illusions when drunk, but this . . ."

"Pick him up," interrupted the captain. "Are you afraid?"

This was too much. Chano would not be called a coward. He walked to the bar, drank a glass of mescal, and with never a word, lifted the corpse from the floor to his back and made off down the trail to the river. Here, he tied a large stone to the *padrecito's* neck and, pushing the body into the stream, remained to watch it sink.

"Now," he said, "Chano Calanche, let yourself not forget what your eyes have seen."

The bandits, having arranged the third corpse as they had the second, awaited the return of the drunkard.

"*Caballeros*, I remember well what my eyes have seen."

"*Oiga*," said the captain, "it is getting late into the night and it is no time for pranks."

"But I lost the *padrecito* and have returned for the best quart of wine in this cantina."

An outlaw who at that moment was standing between Chano and the corpse stepped aside. A bitter expression of disgust came over the drunkard's face as he looked down upon the corpse at his feet. He poured and drank two glasses of mescal, picked up the body, and said, "*Caballeros*, give me an ax. This *padrecito* has annoyed me sorely. No dead man shall stand between José Chano Calanche and the best quart of wine in this cantina."

You like this story, yes? No, no, this isn't all. *Ahora verás* (now you will see). Wait, you must hear the part *más graciosa*.

Bueno, Chano Calanche carried the *padrecito* three miles into the chaparral. Finding a small thicket of dead mesquites, he placed his burden upon the ground, cut wood, and built a large fire. When the blaze had begun to crack and roar with heat, the corpse was thrown in and covered with dry wood.

"You shall never return," said Calanche. "I will see you to ashes and dust before I leave you." He sat himself down upon the ground just out of heat range and watched the burning *padrecito*.

It was daybreak. A priest who was returning to the *villa* from a visit in the country saw the fire and decided to dismount from his mule and warm up a cup of *atole* (corn gruel). He was seated near the small blaze when our drunkard, Chano Calanche, awoke.

"You shameless wretch," screamed Chano. "I put you there to burn, and there you sit preparing a meal over your own funeral fire. I shall teach you a trick. *Ahora verás!*"

The *padrecito* had not seen Chano when he dismounted and was so badly frightened by the latter's shouts and curses that he sprang to the back of his mule and fled.

The best quart of wine was never claimed by José Chano Calanche, and to this day it occupies a place of esteem in the Cantina del Aguililla and is not to be had at any price.

BLANCA FLOR

JUAN WAS A GAMBLER AND HAD LOST everything he possessed. One day of so many he strolled from the town grumbling to the effect that for some money and a bit of luck he would sell himself to the devil. Immediately there reined up before him a man on a large black mount.

"I am the devil," said he; "state your contract."

"Some money to start and five years of unbroken luck," said Juan.

"Granted," replied the devil. "Within five years you are to come to me and perform three commands. You will find me on the Plains of Berlín at the Hacienda of Qui-quiri-quí."

Juan began gambling again, and his devil's luck performed miracles for him. He won money, land, houses, and stock until there was nothing else to be won.

At the end of the *plazo* of five years he set out for the Plains of Berlín and the Hacienda of Qui-quiri-quí, and within a month reached a hermitage. The hermit greeted him and said, "What are you doing in these parts, good man?"

"I'm looking for the Plains of Berlín and the Hacienda of Qui-quiri-quí," said Juan.

"I have lived hereabouts for one hundred years," said the hermit, "and I have never heard of the place. However, I am the ruler of the fishes of the sea. I shall call them and ask them the way to the Plains of Berlín and the Hacienda of Qui-quiri-quí."

Thereupon he whistled three times and the fishes from all depths came to the shore.

"Where are the Plains of Berlín and the Hacienda of Qui-quiri-quí?" asked the hermit.

Not a living form from beneath the waves could make reply.

"Twenty days from here there is a brother older than I," said he. "Surely he will be able to direct you."

Juan traveled twenty days and finally reached the second hermitage.

"What are you doing in these regions?" asked the hermit.

"I'm seeking directions to the Plains of Berlín and the Hacienda of Qui-quiri-quí," said Juan.

"I have lived here over one hundred years," said the hermit, "and I have never heard of the place. However, since I rule the animals of the earth, I shall call them and ask them the way to the Plains of Berlín and the Hacienda of Qui-quiri-quí."

Thereupon he whistled three times and the animals from the forests and the plains and the mountains gathered before his door. But none could make reply.

On the following day the hermit commanded the lion to conduct Juan twenty days to the third and last hermitage.

"Oh, good man," the oldest hermit greeted him, "what seekest thou in this desert land?"

"I'm looking for the Plains of Berlín and the Hacienda of Qui-quiri-quí," said Juan.

"I have lived here for two hundred years," said the hermit, "and have never heard of the place. However, since I rule the birds of the air, I shall call them and ask them to direct thee wherever thou wilt go."

He whistled three times. Birds of every description gathered before him, and he counted them and found the eagle was not there. He whistled again and again, and at the fourth call the large bird lit before the ruler.

"I heard you calling," said he, "but I was far, far away on the Plains of Berlín near the Hacienda of Qui-quiri-quí."

"This eagle knows," said the hermit to Juan. "Tomorrow thou shalt kill six lambs and, with the meat well packed, mount the back of this king of birds."

The following morning the eagle left the earth for the clouds of high heaven, carrying Juan and the pack of six lambs upon his back. From time to time he called for food and Juan fed him, and in the afternoon of that very day he settled down upon the Plains of Berlín not far from the Hacienda of Qui-quiri-quí.

"Look to your right," said the bird. "Go to those baths and wait. Three doves will come there to bathe. They are three beautiful girls. First, two will arrive. You are not to disturb them. They will go away and another will come to bathe. She is the prettiest of the devil's three daughters. Her name is Blanca Flor [White Flower]. As soon as she shall have assumed human form and shall have removed her clothes and entered the bath, you will possess her clothes and refuse to return them until she has agreed to marry you."

Juan did as commanded. He did not bother the first two doves. However, when the third had changed from dove to maiden and had entered the bath, he sat down near her clothes and refused to allow her to leave the water until she had consented to marry him.

Then Juan told his bride why he had come to the Hacienda of Qui-quiri-quí.

"Very well," said Blanca Flor. "However, when you are asked into the devil's mansion, you must refuse, saying you prefer a dirty little hut near the corral; and when you are asked to partake of food, you are to refuse that also, saying you prefer tortillas that are hard, old, and molded."

"Come in, friend Juan," greeted the devil.

"No, *gracias*," said Juan. "I had rather be at home in a dirty little hut near the corral."

"Come dine with me," said the devil.

"No, *gracias*, I am not used to fine foods," said Juan. "I prefer tortillas that are hard and old and molded."

"Very well," said the devil, "within three days I shall make the first of the three demands. Rest well, for it will require strength."

At the end of three days the devil came to the dirty little hut and said, "Juan, tonight you are to fulfill my first demand. Behold that mountain. At midnight pick it up and place it on the other side of the hacienda."

Juan was confused beyond all powers of description. He went to Blanca Flor and explained what was expected of him.

"Don't worry, my love," said she. "I shall shift the mountain for you."

At dawn the devil was asked to view the work. "*Vieja*," said he to his wife, "he has changed the mountain."

"I would say," said the *diabla*, "that our daughter Blanca Flor did that. However, she is locked in her room with seven keys."

Then the devil returned to Juan and commanded him to go the following night and plant an orchard bearing fruit down near the Laguna of Death.

Juan was confused by such a demand and told his troubles to Blanca Flor.

"Don't worry, my love," said she. "I'll plant the orchard for you."

Next morning the devil was asked to view the orchard.

"*Vieja*," he called to his wife, "he has planted the orchard, and the trees are laden with fruit."

"If it weren't for my faith in the lock of seven keys," said the *diabla*, "I would say that Blanca Flor had planted the orchard."

The devil's third demand was that Juan ride a horse that had never known bit, saddle, or spur.

"The horse," said Blanca Flor, "will be the devil himself. Be careful how you enter the corral. Master him with a club. Keep him down as you would a locoed horse; beat him between the ears. Under the shed you will find saddle, spurs, and the bridle. Kick the spurs aside; they are my sisters. Do not touch the saddle, for it is my mother. Be careful with the bridle, however, for it is myself. Bridle, mount bareback, and use the club."

The horse did every trick known to demon, but Juan was not to be thrown. At the end of three hours a panting, sweating, and bleeding horse was led into the corral, and Juan went to the large house and asked that the devil come down to the lot and see how well the horse was broken.

"My master is sick in bed with fatigue and a battered head," said a servant. "He says to tell you that he will see you later."

"That must never be," said Blanca Flor. "We must leave tonight."

At twelve o'clock that night, in some manner known only to the devil's prettiest daughter, Blanca Flor picked the lock of seven keys after having spat four times in her room. Then she and Juan, on the poorest horse in the *remuda*, escaped from the Hacienda of Qui-quiri-quí.

The *diabla*, suspicious of Blanca Flor, came to her door and called, "Blanca Flor!"

"*Mande!*"[1] answered the first spittle.

Later the *diabla* called again. "*Mande!*" answered the second spittle, but rather faintly, for it was nearly dry.

Later, along toward dawn, the *diabla* called again, "Blanca Flor!"

"*Mande!*" said the third spittle, but scarcely above a whisper.

Just as day was breaking over the Plains of Berlín, the *diabla* called again, "Blanca Flor!"

There was no answer. The seven keys, used one after the other, opened the door. Blanca Flor was gone.

The devil gave chase and soon overtook the runaways.

Among the many things that Blanca Flor took with her were a brush and a looking glass. When it had begun to look as if the devil

[1] Literally, *commanded. What is it?*

was sure to catch them, she threw the brush over her shoulder; and when it struck the earth there sprang from the soil a thicket of thorns. After much delay the devil found his way through the brush and had all but caught Juan and Blanca Flor when the latter threw to the earth the looking glass. Immediately it formed a large lake. The devil quit the chase, but the *diabla* continued to follow until she came to a little hut.

"Have you seen a man and a girl pass this way?" she asked the owner of the place.

"*Sandías y melones,*" said the man.

She asked three times, but "Watermelons and cantaloupes" was the only answer she got.

"I shall leave you at this lake until I have made arrangements for our wedding," said Juan to Blanca Flor.

"When you reach your home, embrace no one," said Blanca Flor, "for if you do you will forget me."

Juan reached home and declined to embrace all until, at last, forgetting his promise, he put his arms about an aunt who was ill in bed. He forgot Blanca Flor.

Three days later he arranged to marry another girl. The day of the wedding arrived and everyone for miles around attended. Among the many friends were an old man and an old woman, bringing with them a young woman who just that day had come to their home to live. This girl was very beautiful, and on a green bough she carried were two doves.

"Talk for them, little dove," said the girl. "Tell them about the Hacienda of Qui-quiri-quí and the Plains of Berlín. Tell them of Blanca Flor and a promise that was forgot."

The little dove told the story I have just told you.

"Ay," said Juan, "I remember now. I am Juan the gambler. I sought the Plains of Berlín, the Hacienda of Qui-quiri-quí. With the aid of Blanca Flor, I changed the mountain, planted the orchard, and rode the demon horse. It was Blanca Flor who directed me from those infernal lands to my home and my former self; and this is my wife to be, for this is Blanca Flor."

Juan and Blanca Flor were married. Juan no longer gambles, and they live on a ranch not far from here.

⤴ THE TOOTH OF GOLD

ONCE UPON A TIME THERE WAS AN
old woman who had a vain daughter.

And since the woman was old and poor, she said to the daughter
one day, "*Hijita,* I believe it would be well for you to get married."

"The idea!" laughed the proud young lady. "Just as if there were
a man in the whole world fit for me."

The little old woman made no reply.

"*Mamacita,*" added the girl, "we shall make a bargain, you and
I. Since it is your wish, I will marry; but it must be to a man with a
golden tooth."

Now where there are vanity and pride there is a devil not far
in the offing. A young man knocked at the door.

"My object here will not please you, señora," said the handsome
youth. "I have come to ask for the right hand of your daughter."

"Her happiness is my happiness," said the mother. "*Hija,* you
have heard."

"Yes, mother," whispered the girl, "and also have seen a golden
tooth. I will marry him."

Immediately after the wedding a most unusual thing happened.
The groom, with not so much as a good-bye kiss, left, saying he
would return within three days.

"Mother," said the girl, "what manner of man is this?"

"A strange one, daughter, a very strange one. Perhaps that
comes from the fact that he has a golden tooth."

"What shall I do?" asked the daughter.

"Listen, *hijita,*" said the mother. "Your *santitos* have been long
forgotten. Bring them forth from the closets and trunks; dust them
well; put them on the tables, and hang them on the walls; then pray
to them, *hijita.* Thus the saints may help."

The girl did as she was told to do.

Three days later the husband came home. "What is this?" he
shouted, "what is this? Tear these images down, break them, sweep
them into the patio, and burn them. I can't bear the sight of them."

The young wife was forced to do as told. She took down her
santitos from the tables and the walls, broke them, swept them into
the patio, and burned them.

"Here," said her husband, removing the golden tooth from his mouth. "Here is something better. Now see to it that no *santitos* are brought here again. Also here is some money. I am leaving you again. In three days I shall return."

"Stay with me,'" pleaded the girl. "It isn't *santitos* or golden tooth or money that I want. It is you; I want you."

"You want me?" laughed the man. "You want me? Women have gone to hell for that. *Adiós*."

"Mother, what can this mean?" asked the girl. "He will not lie with me and has left me again. What can it mean?"

"God knows, *hijita*," answered the little old woman. "I will ask the *padrecito*."

"*Padrecito*," said the woman to the priest the following morning after mass, "I have come to you for help. My vain and thoughtless daughter married a man with a golden tooth. In addition to refusing to lie with her, he has compelled her to burn her *santitos*, saying he cannot bear the sight of them. What manner of man is he?"

"Woman," said the *padrecito*, "your son-in-law is the devil."

"God's mercy!" exclaimed the little old woman. "And now, how am I to rid myself of him?"

"Listen to me," said the *padrecito*. "Here is a crucifix. Go to the plaza and buy a mule whip and a jug with a tight-fitting stopper. Take these to your daughter's room, nail a nail in the door, unstop the jug, and place it beneath the bed; and then, with the mule whip, stopper, and crucifix handy await the return of the devil. When he arrives and enters the room, shut the door, hang the crucifix on the nail, and then with the mule whip beat him without mercy. He will wither to the size of a dog and will hide beneath the bed, but don't let up. Lay on the whip until he has withered to the size of a wasp and for safety has crawled within the jug. Then drop the whip and plug the mouth of the jug with the tight-fitting stopper. With this well done, place the jug and its contents in a sack and have it buried six feet underground one league from the village."

The little old mother hastened to the plaza and did as she was told. Having arranged the jug, stopper, whip, and crucifix in convenient order, she seated herself and awaited the return of the devil.

On the third day, as he had promised, the latter returned and entered the room. The *madrecita* closed the door quickly, hung the crucifix on the nail, and turned upon the poor devil with fury. She flogged her bewildered victim until, wailing and screaming, he withered to the size of a dog and fled beneath the bed. She laid on the whip with increased fire until the unfortunate devil shrank to the size of a wasp and crawled into the jug for safety. Then she dropped her whip, snatched up the stopper, and pressed it hard and tight into the mouth of the jug.

Just then she heard someone singing a doleful drunkard's song. It was the village toper on his way down the street to the cantina.

"Listen, man," called the *madrecita*, clapping her hands, "listen; where are you going?"

"I am seeking a Christian who may wish me a happy morning," answered the toper.

"I have an errand for you," said the little old woman. "I will give you thirty pesos if you will take this sack and its contents one league from this village and bury it six feet beneath the ground."

"That is not an errand," said the toper; "that is work. However, just wait a little minute until I find someone to wish me a happy morning. I will return and do this work."

"You need go no farther," said the *viejita*. "Here is a pint of wine. Drink it with my wishes for many happy mornings."

Having drunk the wine, the toper took to the street with shovel, pick, and sack. "I am still thirsty," he thought. "When a man is *crudo* [hung over], his health is easily impaired. I shall spend one of my thirty pesos for a quart of mescal."

He entered a cantina, called for mescal, drank a quart of it, and left.

Presently a weird, buzzing voice called, "*Valecito!*"

"Ha," said the drunk, "only when a man has money does he get such greetings. I'll show them that they are of small import to me."

"*Valecito*," called the weird voice again.

"This grinds me to the marrow," said the toper. "Who's calling "*Valecito*"?

"It is I, *Valecito*," said the voice; "it is I, here on your back. I'm your old friend the devil. Let me go."

"Ah, my old friend the devil, is it? And I am to let you go. Ha, ha, ha, how original you are. Listen, I was to bury you six feet underground; now that I know you, I will make it twelve."

"No, *Valecito*," whined the devil, "you can't do that. Besides, I'm going to make you a master in the art of magic healing. Curses will be simple for you. Merely place your left hand on the affected part and call, '*Valecito!*' The patient will arise and go his way hale and hardy. Now, come, *Valecito*; let me go."

"That's a trap," said the toper; "you are trying to trick me."

"Trick you!" laughed the little wasp, "trick you! Why should I waste my precious time tricking fellows who are constantly deceiving themselves? Be it known that my word is good, *Valecito*, and my contracts are always valid. Let me go."

The toper agreed to the pact; the jug came open with a puff, and a cloud of sulfur smoke mixed with the morning breeze.

The newly made healer returned the pick and shovel to the little old woman and assured her that the job was well done.

Upon reaching his *jacalito* (little shack), the toper nailed a sign above the door. It read, "*El Curandero Maravilloso*. He cures all ills."

In a certain quarter of the village was a dying man. All doctors who had seen him said there was no cure for him, and now, with hope gone, he was slowly giving way to death.

The relatives heard of the Wonderful Healer. They said: "No harm can come from calling him in. Besides, he may cure our brother here. Who knows?"

The Healer was called. After studying the patient attentively, he agreed to effect a cure for one thousand pesos. The family agreed to the price and left the room.

"*Valecito*," called the Wonderful Healer, placing his left hand on the patient's forehead. "*Valecito!*"

"Give him a life pill and he is cured," whispered the devil to the toper.

The life pill was given. Immediately the man arose, called to his brothers, and assured them he was no longer sick. The Wonderful Healer was paid.

"*India*," called the toper upon reaching his home. "*India vieja*," he called to his wife, "it works. I am indeed the Wonderful Healer. In a few days now, if God will help, we shall be rich and at ease for the rest of our lives."

In the meantime, señores, the devil, with the caution of a cat, had observed every move of his mother-in-law. Thirsting for revenge, he spied upon her constantly.

One day the *viejita* was cleansing the patio with a short brush broom. As she bent forward to sweep the ground, her skirts were slightly lifted in the rear.

"Now," said the devil, "this is my chance."

The little old woman fell to the ground with cramps in her abdomen. The girl rushed to the Wonderful Healer and begged him to come quickly, as her mother was dying.

The toper took his satchel and hat and went to the home of the patient. "She is very sick," said he. "Leave the room, close the door, and I will cure her."

He approached the sick woman, laid his left hand upon her abdomen, and called, "*Valecito!*"

"What do you want, *Valecito?*" answered the devil.

"What? Are you in there? Come, *Valecito*, let me cure the woman; I need the money," said the Wonderful Healer.

"No more than I need revenge," answered the devil. "You know how she locked me in a room and beat me without mercy. You know well how she stopped me within a jug and offered you thirty pesos to bury me alive. She deserves no mercy. I will kill her and take her to eternal torment."

"No, *Valecito*," said the toper, "you can't do that. Remember the contract; there was to be no tricking."

"Very well," said the devil, "stand aside, and I will leave her; but from you I will take the power that is rightly mine. From this day on you are no longer the Wonderful Healer." The devil left.

The *viejita* was cured of her mortal ailment, and the toper is drinking again. His only request is that we fill our glasses, lift them high, and wish him a happy morning.

⤙ LA MADRINA MUERTE

NOT FAR FROM A CERTAIN CITY LIVED a poor man. He had a large family, and the youngest child, a boy, was yet to be christened.

One morning the man said to his wife, "I shall not work today; instead I shall seek a godparent for our son."

He had walked only a little way when he met another poor man. "I know that you are looking for a *padrino* for your child," the poor man said. "I will be his godparent."

Not knowing it was God to whom he spoke, the man said, "No, you are too poor; you have nothing to give your *ahijado*."

Farther down the road he met a man of wealth. "I know," said he, "that you are looking for a *padrino*. I will be godfather for your son."

"No," said the father. "You are too rich."

Next he met a woman. It was Death.

"I know," said she, "that you are looking for a godparent. I will be godmother for your son."

"Good," said the man. "Since you are not partial to youth, age, wealth, or poverty, you may be godmother to my son."

It was Death who baptized the child.

Some years later she returned and asked that her godson be allowed to walk with her into the forest.

In the forest La Madrina Muerte plucked a flower and presented it to her *ahijado*, telling him that it would bring him happiness in accordance with how it was used.

"This plant will cure all ills," said she, "and from now on you will be known as the Famous Healer. However, if upon attending a patient, you see me at the foot of the bed, you are to leave him to me."

The Famous Healer had cured many people when he was called to the bedside of the king.

"Cure me," said the monarch, "and my daughter and kingdom are yours."

Though La Madrina Muerte stood at the foot of the bed and forbade the cure, the Famous Healer disobeyed her. Being a good *madrina*, however, she forgave her *ahijado* this, his first offense.

A few days later the princess took seriously ill, and the Famous Healer was called. La Madrina Muerte was there and forbade the cure, but the godson disobeyed her again. The princess, like the king, was cured; and the following day was set for the wedding. But La Madrina Muerte called for her *ahijado* and took him to a dark abode where burning candles represented the souls of dying mortals.

"This," said La Madrina Muerte, pointing to a new candle, "is your soul. When it is burned down, you are to die."

The *ahijado* asked for more life, and La Madrina Muerte placed a small candle on top of the one representing his dying body.

"You have disobeyed," said she, "and you must pay with your life."

So it was that Death's only godson died, and never since has Death served as *madrina* or revealed the name of the life-giving plant.

Chapter Five

⤶ THE DOG THAT RAN TO THE MOON

THIS WAS A MARRIED MAN. THE ONLY members of his family were his wife, his dog, and himself. He took good care of his dog. Once when he had no work, he said to his wife, "I'm going across the mountains to see my *compadre*. It may be possible that he will give me work or a bit of corn for tortillas. Prepare me a lunch."

That evening the señora said to him, "In this *morral* is your lunch."

And he said to her, "Hang it up on a peg in the wall. I am going to leave early tomorrow morning."

The next morning the *compadre* saddled his dog and traveled all day and until the fall of night. At the edge of night he pitched camp, and after eating lunch he fed his dog. The following morning he was on his way, and at nine o'clock he arrived at his *compadre's* hacienda.

"What a miracle!" said the other *compadre*. "We were not expecting you here."

"Since I had no work, *compadre*," said the new arrival, "I thought I would run over to see if there were some way you could help me. My señora has very little food in the house."

Then the wealthy *compadre* said, "It is all very well, *compadre*. I have provisions enough for all of us. You need look for no work. You may spend the night with me."

"Very well," said the visitor.

They entered the house and the rich *compadre* said, "We are to have a race here next week, *compadre*. A stranger has just arrived in town with a *misionero* horse, and they say this horse is very fast. There is a man in town who owns a fast horse also. There is a bet of five thousand pesos and they are going to run five hundred *varas*. In addition to this bet, the one who loses is to give a dance and pay for the music, and the dance is to last for three days. I should like for you to come and attend this race and festival."

"Yes, I shall come," said the poor *compadre*.

So on the following day the rich *compadre* prepared two *fanegas* of corn, two *fanegas* of *frijoles*, two *fanegas* of red chile, and a box of bacon. "Here are some provisions," said he. "Out there in the corral you will find an *atajo* of burros. You will need them to take this food home."

"It will not be necessary, *compadre*," responded the poor man. "Already I have a way to pack these provisions."

"What do you mean?" asked the rich *compadre*.

"Oh, I will pack them on my dog," said the other.

"You don't mean that," said the rich man.

"Oh, yes, I do," said the poor man. "The only thing I shall need further is that you lend me four ropes."

"There in the corral you will find all you need," said the rich *compadre*.

Then the poor man took the four ropes, and in *mancornado* fashion he tied the two *fanegas* of corn, the two of *frijoles*, the two of chile, and the box of bacon to the back of the dog. Then he said to the rich man, "*Compadre*, I am going now."

The rich *compadre* replied, "I shall expect you next week."

"Yes," said the poor *compadre*, "*con el favor de Dios*, I shall return." And with that he left.

Away down the road at nightfall he unloaded his dog and gave her plenty to eat. She was very tired. The next day he packed her again and continued on his journey. As he was going along about six o'clock that morning, a deer ran across the road ahead of him.

The dog gave one wild bark and took after the deer. The man followed the dog, and, fearing that she would lose the pack, he called. But the dog did not return. The man finally went on and arrived at home very sad.

His señora asked, "Well, how did you make out?"

"Very badly," was his response.

"And why?" asked she.

Then continued the *compadre*, "Because the dog packed with all the provisions ran off after a deer. I fear she will lose them. It will be hard getting them all together again."

The *compadre* passed the day waiting and worrying, and at nightfall the dog had not returned. Then said the *compadre* to the señora, "Put me down a pallet out here by the door. I shall listen during the night. Possibly I shall hear the dog barking."

At midnight the dog returned. "*Vieja, vieja,*" the man called, "my dog has returned. She is still packed. Quick! Bring a light."

When the light was brought, they discovered, in addition to the pack of corn, *frijoles*, red chile, and bacon, a deer atop the load.

"Start a fire," said the man. "The dog is very tired; we must cook some of this meat for her." Presently she was fed.

"This is fine," said the man. "Now I shall be able to attend the races."

"I will go also," said the woman.

"Why not?" replied the man.

Early the following morning the dog was saddled, and the man and the woman mounted and were on their way. A good distance down the road night fell and they camped. The following day at nine o'clock they reached their destination, and the day after that they attended the race. There they saw the *cabestro* (hair rope) stretched across the track, the choosing of the *vedoros* (judges), and the horses rearing and fighting to be on the mark.

At last the *santiaguero*[1] was appointed; the horses were placed side by side touching the *cabestro*. Then the *santiaguero* called, "Santiago"; in a second he repeated, "Santiago"; and then a third time he called, "Santiago." Now the horses were off. At about two hundred and fifty *varas* the *caballo misionero* was reaching his fore-

---

[1]The *santiaguero*, starter, properly calls, "Santiago," three times; at the third call the horses should start.

legs out ahead of the other horses; at the end he was fifty *varas* ahead. There were *vivas*, explosions of firecrackers, and music. The dance began and lasted three days and nights.

When the celebration was over, the owner of the dog said to the other *compadre*, "Go over and tell the winner I have an animal I would like to race."

"What do you mean?" asked the *compadre*. "You have no horse."

Then with a wink, the friend replied, "I didn't say *horse*; I said *animal*; tell the winner I have an animal I would like to race."

When the owner of the missionary horse—a horse taken about the country to match against anything put up—heard the proposition, he said, "I will race anything. What are your stakes?"

"Ten thousand pesos," was the reply.

"Then let it be box stakes so that everyone will have a chance to bet one way or the other, and we will race tomorrow."

The following day people arrived on horseback, in oxcarts, and afoot. They bet on the *caballo misionero*. Eight hundred *varas* was to be the distance. The challenger placed three vaqueros twenty-five yards from the end of the track with instructions that they were to wait with ropes down. Said the owner of the dog, "My animal has a hard mouth, and you will have to rope her to stop her."

Soon all was set. The starting line was approached at a trot, and the *santiaguero* called, "Santiago!"

The dog won the race, ran past the three cowboys, jerked their steeds from under them, and broke the ropes. She would have been running still had there been no end to the earth.

It was now late. The jockey dismounted, unsaddled, hung his bridle and spurs on a golden hook in the blue wall that had stopped them, lay down, and went to sleep. The next morning, much to his surprise, his bridle and spurs were not to be found, and the golden hook was gone. He looked everywhere. It was a casual glance into the sky that revealed them. He had hung his bridle and spurs on the horn of the moon, and there they have hung ever since.

The *compadre* and *comadre* are now very rich. And they are still living just over the mountains somewhere this side of the end of the earth.

⌣ JUAN OSO

ONCE UPON A TIME THERE LIVED NEAR a town in the mountains of the west a man and his daughter. Back of his house was a large garden, wherein Aurora, the daughter, spent many hours daily caring for the flowers. Often in the full of the moon she would remain in this garden late into the night. One night while she was seated on a stone bench beneath a tree she fell asleep. A large bear came and took her away.

When she awoke, she was in a cave and a bear sat near the entrance. Presently he went away. Before leaving, he rolled a large boulder against the mouth of the cave.

The father, who was a very rich man, offered a large reward for the return of his daughter. Hunters from far and wide went in every direction in search of the girl. One morning about five years later she was discovered near the cave cutting flowers. A large bear lay asleep nearby.

The hunter who found her called to her and said, "Don't be afraid. I shall not harm you. I've come to take you to your father."

The girl was afraid and ran to the cave. However, before entering, she called to the man, "You had better leave, because this animal may see and kill you."

The man responded, "I'm not afraid. I have a gun. I have come to take you home to your father."

The bear awoke and rushed upon the man, but was shot and killed. The girl was taken to her father's home. The father was happy and paid the hunter the reward.

After some time the girl gave birth, and they named the child Juan Oso (John Bear). This child grew to be a large and uncontrollable boy.

One day the father of the girl said, "I believe it would be well to send Juan to school."

After a few weeks, Juan became well acquainted with all the pupils, and being no longer timid, he tried to play with them. However, he was too rough. He hurt the other children.

He was a very disobedient boy. He respected only his mother. One day while fighting a man, he was shot. Despite his wound, he broke the man's neck with one blow of his powerful fist. His mother put him to bed and before long he was cured. "You see," said his mother, "it doesn't pay to be rude. From now on be a good boy." Juan did not improve in disposition, and before long he ran away from home.

Soon he began drinking and hanging out at saloons. One day while he was drunk a number of men tried to kill him. The police came, and Juan, feeling that he was involved, fled with the others to the mountains. Here he fell in with two who were to be his friends thereafter. One was Aplastaceras (Flattens-out-wax), and the other was Tumbapuertas (Knocks-down-doors). Wherever these three went, they found it easy to rob; for no door could withstand the strength of Tumbapuertas, and Aplastaceras could flatten out any wall as if it were wax. One day while hidden back of an inn, they were surrounded by officers and a great crowd of citizens. When they were taken into the street, a fight began. Police and citizens were thrown right and left. Some were killed and others were crippled. There were no human powers that could withstand Aplastaceras, Tumbapuertas, and Juan Oso.

They went to the mountains again and camped by a river. One of them had stolen a violin, and while he was seated near the river, he began to play. He drew the bow across a string, and behold! there stood before him a soldier. Then he drew the bow across the string four more times, and four soldiers appeared.

The five of them stood at attention and asked, "What do you want?"

And the bandits said, "We are hungry. We want something to eat."

The soldiers went off and presently returned with all kinds of food.

"Attention!" said the musician, and the five soldiers stood at attention. Then the musician took up his violin and played and played until he had created a whole regiment. Then the three, Aplastaceras, Tumbapuertas, and Juan Oso, with their army, returned to the city, laid siege to it, and took it.

They are living there now in great wealth and esteem.

⤙ UA-PA-CHI (KICKAPOO TALES)

IT WAS WHEN GOD MADE THE WORLD. Everybody was happy. The hawk and the sparrow, they danced. Also the bear and the rabbit; and the butterfly and the thunder-cloud danced together, too. All people were happy, but it was all the time dark.

"I don't like the dark," said the rabbit. "I want it to be light, always."

"*A-kui*," said the bear, "no, I must have the dark; I kill people in the dark."

"Then I want a little light," said the rabbit.

"*A-kui, me-sue-aé*; dark all the time."

God awoke.

"Too much talk; I want to sleep," said God.

"I want light," said the rabbit.

"*A-kui*," said the bear; "*a-kui, a-kui.*"

"*No-hi*," said God, "we must settle this. You two talk. The one who talks most, he wins."

Now, Ma-kua was large and fat. He talked slow. Me-sue-a was small and scared. She talked fast.

"*Me-si-me-pe-ko-te*," said Ma-kua, "*Me-si-me-pe-ko-te*; let it be always dark."

"*Uá-pa-chi, uá-pa-chi, uá-pa-chi*; daylight, daylight, daylight," said the rabbit.

She won. That's why we have light.

The bear loses and will fight. He catches rabbit by the rump and by the nose. Rabbit ran away, but scars show where the bear caught her. These scars are near her eyes and tail. Have you seen them?

The goose and sparrow hawk dance and then fight. Hawk wants most food. God says, "Too much talk; I want to sleep."

Hawk and goose are talking all the time.

"*Na-hi*," said God, "you two run race."

The goose is slow, and the hawk is fast. The hawk laughs at goose. They fly to the sea. Hawk flies fast a while, then rests, then eats a rabbit, then flies again. Goose flies high, goes with the clouds, all the time flying, no stopping to eat and sleep.

When the hawk reaches sea, goose is there.

That's why goose doesn't work for food, and that is why the hawk must always work.

Thundercloud and butterfly dance and then fight. Thundercloud will have all the flowers and runs butterfly out of his garden. They fight and talk.

God says, "You two, too much talk. Thundercloud too much noise. I want to sleep."

Butterfly and thundercloud talk all the time.

"*Na-hi,*" said God, "you two run race to sea."

Thundercloud laugh so loud boulders roll from mountain, and Me-me-ke hides beneath a leaf.

"You two run race," said God.

Wind, thundercloud's friend, no longer friend; now helps butterfly. He loves butterfly. He takes butterfly to sea.

That's why butterfly owns all the flowers, and that's why thundercloud roars with anger.

Goat herder herding goats. Rain falls and creeks and rivers run over banks.

"*Ku-u,*" says goat herder, "*neh-pe nah-ne,* water falls everywhere all the time. Goats must go high on hills."

He drives goats high and water comes high up the hill. Lions, bears, wolves, and cats learn to eat deer, goats, and cows.

Water goes down to creeks and rivers again.

⤆ EL QUE CANTA SUS MALES ESPANTA

THIS MAN WAS A MAN WHO LIVED IN the Kingdom of Ururú. By his friends he was called Chanito. And this name, it seems, came from Chano, and Chano from Borrachán, and Borrachán from the fact that he was a tippler.

Indeed, he wasted so much time and money in the bars that he eventually found himself in the gutter with neither friends nor funds, and this hard circumstance forced him to conquer his bread on the highways and byways of the land.

And so it came about that upon one of so many, many days of wandering he met a man who, for a time at least, was destined to be his one and only friend. This *hombre* was a dealer in fine wines, and he ran a cantina on the central plaza of the capital of the Kingdom of Ururú. But this one and only friend was no common cantinero with nothing more than a strong penchant for the almighty peso. He had a weakness for song, poetry, *la facilidad de la palabra,* and philosophy. Chanito appealed to his whims and intrigued him with such sayings as:

"Look, *amigo,* my vice, as you know and I know and everyone knows, is the *copa.* But in the game of life I am no rogue; I do not play with loaded dice," and "I like people who make a noise when they walk and sense when they talk; no rodeo, no subtle evasions, no traps."

One morning Chanito stopped at the cantina on the main plaza for conventional greetings and the customary *copita.* "*Quiubo,*" he shouted, "*qué tal y cómo le amaneció?*"

There was no response. Toni, for this was the cantinero's name, sat behind the bar staring into space, a tragic picture of one who has been condemned and executed and is ready for the grave.

"*Oiga,* Toni," said Chanito, "first a drink and then out with the news. Tell me, have I pulled a *patraña?* What burdens your soul? Has someone done *mi amigo* something, perhaps? If I can help, I'm at your service. What's the trouble?"

"No, nothing is the matter," came a voice from the living dead. "It is only that I am to solve a riddle by tomorrow morning, and if there is no solution I lose my hide."

"What hide, by the life of me! Is that all? Look, Toni, by the shades of all depths and little demons, don't be foolish. Riddles are child's play."

"Only this riddle is no child's play and it has no solution, Chanito," moaned Toni.

"*Bien, bien;* let's have a drink and then *manos a la obra,*" said Chanito. "So little riddles we have, eh?"

"There is no use," said Toni. "Yet, if you insist, this is the way the cards are stacked. This morning while I was on my way to open my shop, Satan prompted me to sing a little song you taught me; and *peor que peor,* I was passing the palace gates as I sang it."

"So, what?" urged Chanito.

"In less time than it takes to say *santiamén,* I was arrested and taken before His Majesty, the King of the land."

"And charged with *lese magestad,* maybe?"

"No; accused of singing a song of propaganda, a song of reaction, that song of yours called 'Money Is All.'"

"*No le hace;* songs of reaction, flirtations with Her Royal Highness, or stealing the King's ducks—the crime is *lese magestad.* And just for that you are to be skinned alive? *Mire, patrón,* the old law of tooth for a tooth fits this to a T. The King is foolish . . ."

"Sh," warned Toni, "the walls have ears."

"What walls, what ears, and what lost niño! As I have said, the King is foolish. All royalty has one easy virtue. They pride themselves on their word, that is to say, a king's promise given. Surely he promised you something if you solve the riddle."

"Just my hide."

"Magnanimous of him, indeed. Well and good, we will play with His Majesty. We will stake our all on the Knave; that is to say on his weaknesses, his one convenient virtue, '*palabra del rey* [the King's word].' But now, in order to help you I must know the nature and wording of the riddle."

"It is this, Chanito; tomorrow morning I am to tell him how much money will be required to teach a burro to read."

"I presume His Highness is to provide the time and tuition," said Chanito. "We will take him at his word, '*palabra del rey,*' and we will say one thousand pesos in advance and one year."

"By my life, Chanito, no! Burros are burros. Who can teach a burro to read?"

"You, of course. Don't you remember? *Con el dinero todo se hace.* [Anything can be done with money]. Ha, ha, *que risa me da.* [What a laugh.] You yourself sang it. Perhaps you were not thinking. Perhaps you sang to cheer your heart and to frighten away some sad obsession. But such vague excuses would not hold before His Majesty's court. You and I will teach the burro to read and our *lema* [motto] will be *Keep your eye on the Knave,* and

> *No te aflojes,*
> *Ni te apoques.*"

The next morning Toni went to the palace, gave his answer, and asked for the thousand pesos in advance—*palabra del rey*.

"One year, one thousand pesos, and your burro will read?" asked the King.

"Yes, Your Majesty."

Toni and Chanito bought a burro and for three days fed him nothing. They made a book of boards for leaves, and they covered the boards or leaves with symbols resembling the Chinese alphabet; and the leaves they hinged with rawhide. Then they put oats between the boards, and the burro soon learned to turn them to secure his food.

At the end of the year they took their educated ass to court and . . . what amazement! The animal turned the pages leaf by leaf, and finding nothing to eat brayed and brayed. And the people cheered and cheered.

"You win," said the King. "But this isn't all. I will give you a *plazo* of one day to tell me how long and how much money it will take to teach this animal to talk, and mind you, he is to talk a human tongue, and further there will be no advancement of funds this time."

Toni had no heart for more than one small question: *"Palabra del rey?"*

"Palabra del rey."

Chanito was waiting at the cantina when Toni came in. "What's wrong? You look worse than you did before. Didn't I warn you to watch for traps?"

"No traps, Chanito, just a new riddle, and this time if I fail to answer I am to be hanged. He demands now to know how long and how much money it will take to teach our burro to talk."

"Válgame Dios, Toni!" said Chanito. "And just for that you lose your stirrups? It is merely a matter of a new deal in which we substitute guts for heart—you remember the old saying, '*de tripas corazón*'—and if it comes to the worst, who cares? At birth a man is marked for death; we *are* today, and tomorrow *away*. Ha, ha. A fig for death. Come, *amigo*, this is no time for worry."

"But what am I to do?" asked Toni.

"As we have done, Toni; as we have done. Remember, we stake all on the Knave as we did before, *palabra del rey*. Tell him, for a *plazo* of one hundred years and one million pesos we will teach our burro and a whole republic of burros to talk."

An argument followed, for Toni limped on the side of scruples. "An ass is an ass," he said. "Never can we teach this animal to talk."

"Listen, Toni; who cares? Don't you see? One hundred years from now the King, you, the burro, and the one who drives him will be at best a memory, *y nada más. No le parece? No hay mal que cien años dura.*"

I had no time to listen further to this marvelous sense and nonsense, and I regret I do not know *a ciencia cierta* the end of the yarn. However, I do know that some days later I found Chano, alias Chanito, alias Borrachán, just across the border from the wonderful Kingdom of Ururú; and he was all spiderfoot with liquor, and he was staggering x's and s's with his legs and was as happy as a loony lark. And he was singing:

> *De cuatro pares de pantalones*
> *No más me quedan los puros botones.*
>
> . . . .
>
> If more of this you wish to know
> Just go and ask the mamma crow,
> For some opine that it was she
> Who got this first from the ceiba tree.

PERIQUITO, WOOD DEALER

THIS IS A STORY ABOUT A PARROT. AND like most parrots, he saw too much, heard too much, and talked too much. However, this bird talked and talked until he, like some people, became presumptuous and proud. He was proud of his cap of gold and his green suit, proud of the purity of his speech, and proud of his place in society. Yet the thing that amused and annoyed the family with whom he lived was Perico's hatred for the cat and the dog. Nothing appealed more to his parrot sense of humor than to bite the tip of the kitty's tail and to sound false alarms by whistling to the dog. But the hateful pranks he played on the other pets and his love for languages have little to do with this story. Some day, if you will be good *niños*, I will tell you how he lost the feathers from his tail by mistaking a young leopard for a house cat; or how, another time, he talked himself into a job of teaching languages to other parrots.

But, as I have suggested, this story deals with presumption; how he took it upon himself to purchase supplies for the family, and the price he paid for his error.

Well, the señor, señora, and the *niños* were away for the day and the cook was asleep when the vendor of stovewood came down the alley back of the house. He called, "*Leña, leña! Quién quiere comprar leña? Leña, partida, leña partida-a-a.*"

Perico heard this, and the devil prompted him to call out in the voice of his master: "*Dos cargas.*"

The *leñero* stopped his burros and led two of them that were heavily packed with stovewood through the rear door of the large patio. He unloaded the wood, stacked it neatly in a corner as he had done so often before, and waited for the señor to pay the bill. Finally he said to himself, "*Mi patrón* is busy, no doubt. I shall return tomorrow for the money."

He led the two burros through the large door, closed it, and proceeded on down the alley with his *hatajo* (little herd) shouting, "*Leña, leña-a-a!*"

The next day, before leaving town for the *monte*, he dropped by the place where he had left the two *cargas* of split wood to collect for it.

"What are you talking about?" asked the *patrón*. "You must be a bit *toma'o.* I ordered no wood."

"Oh yes you did," said the *leñero*. "I was not in my cups when I entered town, and I came down the alley and called, '*Leña, leña,*' as I have always done. And you answered, '*Dos cargas,*' as you have always done. By the mother of God I swear it."

"*Poco a poco,* Lencho," said the *patrón*. "I was out of town, my family was out of town. Only the cook was here, the cook and the dog, and the cat, and . . ."

And then an amused look mixed with resentment played about the eyes and lips of the *patrón*. "*Está bueno,* Lencho. There has been an error, but we can use the wood. Here is the money."

And then the *patrón* went about the house calling, "*Perico, periquito; quiere nueces, periquito?*"

Presently he heard the parrot answer, "*Corra, corra* [run, run]" which translated from parrot Spanish means, "Make it snappy."

Periquito got no nuts and not even so much as a dry tortilla. He got instead the flogging of his life; and only after he had bitten his *amo's* finger, did he get away. He fled from the back porch into a bedroom and hid beneath the bed.

In the meantime the cook had surprised the cat stealing cream. Kitty too had got a flogging—a good one—and he too had hidden beneath the bed and was there licking his wounds and trying to gather his wits when the parrot, in a great hurry, joined him. Now, as I have said, these two were not on speaking terms, but when Periquito saw the cat's bleeding ear, broken tail, and black eye, he became highly elated.

He laughed and said with affected sympathy, "*Oiga, carajo,* how many loads of wood did you order?"

⌐ NO POOCH 'EM

AND THIS WAS A PARROT WHO TALKED too much. He was an old, old parrot that had been with the family for generations. You know these birds, like elephants, are not plagued by time.

The *perico* of this story became more loquacious as the years went by, and he developed such a disregard for the sensitivities of others that the children in the family wanted to know why he used words they were not permitted to use. The mother, with much embarrassment, explained, and failing to convince the *niños* went to the husband.

"Listen, Juan. This parrot is scandalous. The words he uses in the presence of the children and my friends are embarrassing. And when he lets go a filthy word, he says it *a secas*, with not so much as *con su permiso*. We must get rid of him."

"I heard what you said at first, but I don't understand the last. Did you say 'get rid of him'? If you did, the answer is *vete a pasear, no, a-kui,* and *no* in all the languages of Babel. Don't you realize what you are saying? Periquito is a member of the family, indeed more of a member than you or I. He belonged to *mi mamacita* and before that to *mi abuelita*."

"*Basta*," said the wife. "It's either Periquito or the family. Choose for yourself. Let me know before tomorrow." And out of the room she stormed.

At first Juan was only amused. "Her melodrama sins by over-play," he said. "She doesn't mean it." Then after that he became serious and went to the patio to take a siesta on a cot in the shade of a pomegranate tree.

His sleep was a half-sleep. He saw his wife riding a broom like an old witch and Periquito flying from room to room. His wife was swearing and Periquito, scandalized, was trying to cover his ears with his wings. And presently an owl said, "Halt, I have the answer."

Juan awoke. He sat as if entranced. "The owl," said he, "how in the name of Satan did he enter this crazy *maraña* of domestic troubles?"

And then his countenance began to glow like a *mañanita* in August. He sprang to his feet and called, "María, María, I have the answer! The owl is the answer."

At lunch the cook had complained of an owl that had been eating the chickens. "We must kill the owl or build a chicken house," said she. "As long as these little animals roost in a tree, it will be like in the story of the coyote and the *ranchero*; that is to say a chicken a day until all are gone."

"I have the answer!" shouted Juan to María, his wife. "We will take Periquito from his *percha con to-i cadenita*. We will chain his foot to a limb of the tree where the chickens roost. The owl will keep him awake all night and he will have to sleep by day. And *se acabó* with his swearing. Besides," he added, "maybe the talk of the *inocente* will frighten the owl away, and we will have more *pollo con arroz*, and the cook will be pleased, and you will be happy, and I can go about my business with no further bother."

María consented, for she was now ashamed of her tantrum, and she could see in this arrangement an opportunity to save face.

Bueno, Periquito was chained to a limb of the tree on which the chickens were accustomed to roost. And that night came Señor Tecolote, saw the new chicken with a golden cap and green dress, and lit on the limb beside him.

Well, you know the habits of owls are strange. They won't kill a chicken on the roost. Motivated by instinct or perhaps sportsmanship, they push the victim off the roost and catch it on the fly, and away they go.

Bueno, the Señor Tecolote gave Periquito a slight push. Periquito was a bird of culture despite his profanity. He moved along the limb to give room to the stranger. The latter, however, pushed again.

"*Oiga,* Señor," said Periquito, "*no me empuje* [don't push me]."

"Who?" said the owl, and gave another push.

"*Pues no me empuje, amigo. No ve usted que se me acaba la rama* [Don't you see that I've run out of limb]?"

"Who?" said the owl and pushed again.

"This fellow," mused Periquito, "must be a *gringo* and can't understand."

Then, resorting to Spanish, Kickapoo, parrot talk, and a lot of vulgarity, he said in part, (with *permiso de las señoras*), "*Tate quieto, gringo sala'o,* you—censored and censored and censored again—no pooch 'em! don't push!"

◟ JUAN SOLDADO

                      THIS FELLOW JUAN, AFTER SPENDING some time in the army, asked for his discharge. His final pay was eighteen pesos and eighteen centavos. He bought three *pedazos* of bread and took to the road in the direction of his *tierra.* Barely had he begun his hike for home when he encountered an old man seated beside the road.

"I am hungry," said the old man. "Give me, if nothing more, just a piece of bread."

Juan didn't know this man, but he was San Pablo. Juan gave him one of three pieces of bread he carrried in his *mochila* and continued on his way.

Presently he met another old man who sat begging beside the road. This stranger was San Pedro. Juan grumbled an uncomplimentary word to himself about a republic of beggars, gave the *pordiosero*—or San Pedro—the second piece of bread, and passed by.

Farther up the road he met another beggar. This old man was God. Juan, not knowing God, became angry. But after a tirade of unspeakable words, he calmed down and gave away his last piece of bread. The old man smiled and said:

"I see you don't speak always from the heart. You are a good man, and just for that I give you my blessings, and of many *mercedes* I possess I shall give you one for the bread you gave me. What will it be? *Sea lo que fuere.*"

"Oh," said Juan, "I would like to believe that my knapsack has some magic power."

"Granted," said God. "Now when you need anything, just say, 'Todo a mi mochila,' and whatever you wish will enter your knapsack." They said good-bye.

Juan came to a small town, and while on his way down a street he saw a large plate of sweet food in a window. He was hungry but did not care to spend the little money he had for sweets.

But then he thought of the old man's blessings. With a dubious grin he gave a command as if he were a sergeant: "Todo a mi mochila." Immediately the plate of sweet food disappeared from the window, and his pack seemed to grow heavier.

At nightfall he came to a town and asked for a place to sleep. There was no hotel, no inn, no place at all where a stranger could spend the night. Finally he found an old, abandoned house, but as he entered a man advised that he sleep elsewhere, that the place was the abode of ghosts.

"Everyone who sleeps there," said the stranger, "wakes up dead."

But this fellow Juan was a man of much valor, and he entered the house and made his preparations to spend the night there.

About midnight he heard the rattle of small stones on the roof. He was unable to sleep, and eventually he heard voices. They chanted: "Caigo, o no caigo; caigo, o no caigo."

"Caigan!" said Juan.

The chanting ceased, and Juan saw a legion of devils standing before him.

"Todos a mi mochila," he ordered. And they entered his knapsack.

Juan is rich now. He uses these devils in his financial dealings. But every night before going to bed he puts his money in a bank.

⤸ LA CENICIENTA HUASTECA

MARÍA LA CENICIENTA WAS A GIRL
who worked for a woman who had a daughter. She had to do all
the housework and besides was compelled to labor at night carding
wool. However, there was a little lamb that helped her. And this
story tells us that the woman learned about this and ordered the
lamb killed. Also, she called this girl, La Cenicienta, and told her
to take the stomach of the lamb to the river and wash it and prepare it for *menudo*. While she was at the river preparing the meat
for *menudo* some fish came and carried the little stomach away. La
Cenicienta began to cry.

Then a fairy woman appeared and told her to weep no more.
She said that near by La Cenicienta would find a small house and
in the house was a baby crying and some large *tinajas* (ollas) turned
upside down.

"Sing to the baby and put it to sleep," she said; "then turn the
tinajas upright."

La Cenicienta did as that fairy woman ordered. She found the
small house and the baby crying. She sang and the little one went
to sleep. Then she turned a *tinaja* upright, and immediately a
golden star fixed itself upon her forehead and she was dressed in
fine clothes. She turned another *tinaja* and there found the *menudo*
meat prepared for cooking.

When she returned home the woman and the girl wanted to
know how she got the fine clothes and the star. La Cenicienta told
them what had happened at the river.

Envy entered the hearts of the woman and the girl, and they
took the clothes from La Cenicienta. Then the woman had another
lamb killed and sent her daughter to the river with the stomach of
the animal.

"Do as La Cenicienta did," she said. "You will get more beautiful things."

The daughter took the meat to the river and while she was
washing it, some fish came and carried the little stomach away.
Then the girl pretended to weep. A fairy woman came to her and
said:

"Weep no more. Go to the little house near here. You will find a baby crying. Sing it to sleep. Then the *tinajas* you see in the house are to be turned upright."

That girl went to the small house, and she whipped the baby hard. She turned a *tinaja*, and the *moco* of a *guajolote* (a turkeycock's comb) attached itself to her forehead. She went home and wrapped a cloth about her head to hide the *moco*.

Later, the woman and her daughter went to mass. La Cenicienta was in the kitchen weeping and working when a fairy woman came to her and asked why she was sad.

"I wanted to go to mass," said La Cenicienta, "but they wouldn't let me." And then the fairy woman gave her a wand of *virtud*. "When you wish with your heart for something that is good, touch the star on your forehead with this wand and your wish will come true," she said.

Immediately La Cenicienta wished for elegant clothes and golden shoes and a carriage *mejor que ninguno* with a span of fine horses.

She went to mass. Everyone was amazed, and a prince fell in love with her.

When later the woman and her daughter came home, they found La Cenicienta in her ashy clothes working in the kitchen as usual. They told La Cenicienta of the miracle that they had seen at mass.

"The miracle was I," said La Cenicienta.

They laughed and mocked and said the star on La Cenicienta's forehead was taking the salt from her brain.

The following Sunday the woman and daughter went to mass, and as before left La Cenicienta home. However, this time La Cenicienta did not weep. She used her wand of *virtud* as she had done before, and behold she was at mass as beautiful as the most beautiful fairy.

When La Cenicienta left the church she lost one of her golden shoes near the door. The prince found it and went to the home where the woman lived with her daughter. He said he intended to marry the girl whose foot would fit that shoe. The woman's daughter crammed her big foot into the shoe. The prince put her in the carriage and was on his way to his palace when a little dog began barking and saying, "*Moco de guajolote va en coche y estrella de*

oro está en casa (the turkey-cock's comb goes in the carriage, and
the star of gold is in the house)." The prince was puzzled and went
back to the house where the woman lived. He found the beautiful
servant La Cenicienta. The golden shoe fitted her foot. They were
married, *y fueron muy felices.*

Chapter Six

⤳ JUAN DE TOLUCA

THE KING AND THE QUEEN HAD BEEN married thirty years, and they had had no children at all, not one. One day the queen told the king that she was going to have a baby and that it was her wish that it be baptized by a little old man who lived out in the mountains, a woodcutter. And the king said that he had no objections to this.

The following day the king sent some troops to open a road into those mountains so that he could go in person to invite the wood-cutter and his wife to the baptism. And when the road was finished the king took a buckboard and went to the place where the little old people lived.

When the king invited them they asked if it were true that they were to have such a great honor as that of being godparents with the king. And the latter said that it was true indeed. Then the little old man said that if this was the desire of Their Majesties, he and his wife would accept. Then the king departed.

The next day the king sent some servants with clothing and provisions and with orders that the little old people be fed and bathed and properly clothed.

One week later the child was born, and the king went to the mountains and returned with the little old people.

At birth the child had teeth and could talk. The little old people entered the king's house to congratulate the queen. And then they went to see the baby, and the baby greeted them. They were amazed and said, "*Comadre*, the child has teeth and can speak."

And then the baby said to the queen, "Have them give my *tata padrino* a purse of reales to be scattered among the poor on the way to the baptism."

After the baptism the king gave a banquet that lasted eight days. And then the little old man told the king that he could not be away from his home *tanto día*, that his house had no one to look after it. Then the baby told the king to send servants to care for the house until *tata padrino* could return home.

After the eight days of banqueting the baby said to the king, "Give my *tata padrino* two bags of reales so he won't have to work as a woodcutter."

The little old people returned to their home in the mountains, and the *viejito* said to his wife, "All the same I am a worker; I must cut wood."

The following day he went to the *monte* and didn't return until late at night. And then the woman said, "Where is the wood you went to get?"

"I cut no wood. I spent the day catching this lion cub I have here."

And the old lady said, "What do you want with that animal?"

The *viejito* answered: "I want to take him as a gift to our godson. This will be something he can play with."

And the little old woman said, "Yes, and that lion will eat our godson."

The following day the *viejito* loaded on a small wagon what wood he had about the place and went to the city. He greeted the king and the queen and his godson, and said his only purpose in the city was to present a small lion cub to his godson.

The present was accepted, and since the child was small and the lion was small, the queen ordered a servant girl to keep the lion near the cradle so that the two would become accustomed to each other.

The pet and the little prince grew as the months went by and they learned to play together and to understand one another. The lion never abandoned the boy.

One day the king asked the queen: "How are we going to separate the two? The lion is getting large and some day he is likely to harm the child. I'm afraid we will have to kill the animal."

The lion heard this; and since he was a prince that had been enchanted years ago along with three cities, he understood what was said.

"I am leaving," he said to the boy. "The king wants to kill me so that you will be alone."

"If you go," said the boy, "I am going with you."

That night they ran away and took to a large range of mountains. The lion provided the boy with food and water and watched over his sleep to protect him from wild beasts.

Within fifteen days they had crossed the mountain range and had come to a large sea. Then the lion said to the boy, "Look; at this place you are going to mount on my back and we will cross this sea."

They crossed to the other shore and continued to travel.

Then the lion said: "Now I am going to put a legend on your forehead that will read, 'I am Juan de Toluca.' Then you will change suddenly from a little boy to manhood. And then you are to enter that city yonder in the sunset's gloaming. A king who has three daughters lives there, and on the door of the castle there is a sign that says, 'To that one who can cause the dead vines in my vineyard to bear fruit again will be given one of my three daughters in marriage.' Go into the city, find the palace, knock at the door, and tell the king that you will cause the dead vines to bear fruit again."

The next day the boy went to the king's house and knocked at the door. The king came out and said, "What are you doing around here, Juan de Toluca?"

And the boy said, "I was on my way by when I saw this sign on your door, and I have decided to make your vines green up and bear fruit again."

"Come in," said the king.

"I did not come to visit," said Juan. "*Yo, a lo que vengo, vengo.* Tomorrow have ready a hoe, a spade, and a bucket. Good-bye."

With no more magic than hard work and water, Juan caused the vines to green up and produce. He borrowed a basket and pan from the king and returned with fruit of many varieties.

"Come in, Juan de Toluca," said the king.

"I did not come to visit," said Juan. "*Yo, a lo que vengo, vengo.* Now I want your youngest daughter." After considerable haggling the king agreed to the demand. The princess and Juan were married and went immediately to the mountains. There they found a castle instead of a cave.

"How did this happen?" asked Juan.

"*Son cosas mías,*" was the lion's answer.

The two older daughters of the king ordered spies to follow Juan and their sister. These spies found the castle in the mountains and directed the sisters to it. They were amazed at the wealth and beauty of the place, and when they returned home they told their father the king all about it.

"Fine," said the king. "Now that I have a war on my hands with the Moors, I will have Juan lead my army. He will be killed, my army will whip the enemy, and we will get the castle in the mountains."

After arrangements were made for Juan to lead the king's armies, the lion called him aside and said: "Let the army precede you. After the forces are gone, then I shall change into a poor horse; you mount me, and I shall take you beyond the black lagoon. When I jump in you are not to fall off. On the other side you are to kill all the Moors *a puros machetazos*; then the war will be over."

When Juan reached the field of battle he found the king's forces in flight. He killed all the Moors and returned to the mountains on his poor horse.

The king, upon learning what had happened, said: "We will try another scheme to rid ourselves of Juan. Tomorrow there will be a *corrida de toros*. One of the three bulls will surely kill him."

The lion heard of this, went to Juan, and said: "Juan, tomorrow you are to be a bullfighter. The three bulls are enchanted cities. You are to kill them. This once accomplished, the people will be free again and I shall regain my form as prince. You are to keep one of the cities; the second city will belong to me; and the third is to be governed by your *tata padrino* for his part in my disenchantment."

The bulls were killed and three *mesas* became three cities, ruled by the lion now a prince, Juan de Toluca and his queen, and Juan's *tata padrino*.

◟ CHISOS GHOSTS

WILLIAM WEBER, OFTEN ACCOMPANIED *by his sons Ferdinand and Phillip, made many trips into the mountains of the Big Bend in search of Spanish gold. Once I, a skeptic, and especially* desconfiado *in matters dealing with buried treasure, went along with the party in search of $70,000,000. We did not find the money, but I came out with three folktales, one* corrido, *one* chupaderro *stone, a rusty part of an old stagecoach once owned by my uncle Dave Aiken, and a lead on a story I had heard as a child in 1904 on the Alamo de Cesaria Ranch and stage stand. This story was grand. Ghosts were legion, and the tragedy was Wagnerian.*

Some day I hope to go into the Chisos Mountains again, and you may bet your boots I won't be looking for Spanish gold. Instead I shall have a weather ear out for further details of this story. Until I find them, I am thankful for such gajitos *as follow. These bits I shall give you in Ferdinand Weber's words, as he told them to me in conversation on August 29, 1930, in Marfa, Texas.*

The Bofecillos range of mountains is about eight miles from the Rio Grande in the southeast corner of Presidio County. It is said that the name comes from the Spanish word *bofes*, which means lungs. Some say they doubt this, since the *c* in the word would, in that case, have been *s*. *Bofe* can also mean fool; and if the word Bofecillos should be derived from *bofe*, then the range must have been named for the kind of Indians who made their home there.

Tradition has it that many years ago a trail ran through this range of mountains from Chihuahua and that sometime after the independence of Mexico from Spain much treasure was packed through here to be hoarded in San Antonio. One pack train was ambushed, and the guards and *arieros* were killed and buried with the treasure.

Some years later strange things began to happen in this region. Ghosts were seen, bells were heard, and flames of fire, usually after a heavy rain, would flare from the tops of the mountains. On Good Friday, 1927, many reports of ghosts, bell sounds, and flames came from the Bofecillos. I was in the mountains at this time with a party of four. One afternoon I heard the bells. I listened. The sound ceased. There was only the wail of a lone coyote out among the sotols. At the time I was leading the pack mule at the head of the line traveling an old trail Indian-like. I was worried. I knew I had heard bells but preferred to keep this fact to myself.

"Could it be," I thought, "could it be that a buckle has come in contact with the skillet atop the pack?"

I stopped, dismounted, and checked the pack. My friends were more quiet than usual. I picked up a small rock and tapped the skillet. Without knowing what I was doing, I looked up into the face of one of my buddies. His face was solemn, his eyes were large, and he was pale.

"That ain't it," he said.

"Bells?" I asked.

He nodded and spat on the ground.

Then I began examining our surroundings. It was possible that the sounds we heard were made by the wind. In front of us and to the north was a large, open draw, covered with big mesquite trees and wild grapevines. All was still. And then the chiming began again, and continued for seven minutes.

The men in this party, besides myself, were R. L. Ramey, a man by the name of Stevenson, Vivián Luján of Marfa, and a Mexican from San Antonio.

Later the same day, sometime between dusk and dark, as we walked along the edge of a bluff of overhanging rock near our camp, my companion stopped and began to show signs of excitement. Naturally, I asked what was wrong.

"Don't you see the fires? Spirits of the Chisos?" said he.

Finally, as the night drew on I too saw flames, at a point some three-fourths of a mile away. They were silver white, about one foot in width and three in height. They flared up twice and I saw them no more. However, to the south about two miles I saw two more flares. One was green and the other was red.

Before making this trip I had talked to Father Palomo. He said that in the early days the Jesuits were able to find treasures, and it was their belief that this could be done best during Lent. At this time the spirits of the dead who had been buried with treasure begged for mercy, and their petitions were expressed in mystery fires.

Many ghosts have been seen in the Bofecillos. Some years ago a man who said he was hunting horses saw from a distance what he took to be a man seated on a rock. The horse hunter decided to approach him and to ask if he had seen any horses—one small bay in particular. Upon coming near this man the cowhand's horse began to shy. Finally he got close enough to the supposed man to make out that he was not a man at all, but a spiritlike something that spoke and asked what a rider might be looking for in those parts. The rider said he was looking for a small bay horse.

The spirit said: "Never mind the little bay. Come with me, and I will show you something worth far more than a horse." The mount got plumb spooked and began pitching and running. But the ghost, in the meantime, had caught a stirrup. Although by now the horse was running at full speed, the ghost hung in. It was dragged through thorn brush and over stones, and at last, in disgust, it turned loose with this expression: "*Vete, pues, ingrato; yo trataba de ayudarte* (go, then, ingrate; I tried to help you)."

Again, at another time, a man and his family were traveling by wagon on a road near where the ghost, whose name was Manuel el Curito, had tried to catch the cowhand. The family camped at this place for the night. After dark they became aware of the fact that someone was tossing pebbles at them. This noise scared the man and his family. They climbed into the wagon and sat all night listening to the pebbles falling on the wagon cover. Next morning they left and made good speed until they were well out of the Bofecillos.

Still again, near here, a cowhand rode up to a mulberry bush and was eating mulberries when he heard a woman's voice calling to him. Upon looking toward an overhanging cliff he saw an angel, who motioned for him to approach. He did otherwise, and went yon to far places in great haste and left heel dust and the angel behind him.

Some years ago three Mexicans came into Marfa from Mexico. They hired a guide to take them to the scene of the Chisos treasure. They were digging one day not far from the mulberry bush where the cowhand had seen the angel, when something made them aware that someone was watching them. Upon looking down the slope they saw six Indians mounted on fat ponies—two paints, two sorrels, and two duns. These ponies were bridled only with *bozales*, or headstalls. The Mexicans pulled up and left for Marfa. They said it was useless to dig for treasure so long as the spirits stood guard.

If the reader has no belief in ghosts, I suggest he buy, borrow, or steal a horse and ride into the Bofecillos, make a camp all by his lonesome, stake his mount, eat supper, and then listen to the weird mystery of Chisos voices in the canyons and watch for ghost fires.

⤷ DON JUAN ZURUMBETE

THIS WAS A FELLOW WHO WAS WITHOUT depth in everything except the cup. He was a misfit and drifter, and his very lack of character was his character. It was said that the only thing he ever did right was the wrong thing. Once a young friend took him to task and said: "Listen to me, Juan. You are on your way down and out. Get hold of yourself before it is too late. Remember the old saying:

> *Agua que va río abajo*
> *Arriba no ha de volver.*"

To this Juan replied with affected solemnity: "Your intentions are good, *amiguito*, but surely you haven't forgotten what is said of good intentions. Furthermore, *amigo de mi alma*, my life is *muy mía* and is of more import to me than to you. You commune with an arbitrary principle and I with a bottle. *Y qué!* So what! And as for the waters of a river once downstream being downstream forever, my answer is: *A otro perro con ese hueso* (go to another dog with that bone)."

And the friends went their respective ways, one to a temple and the other to the nearest saloon.

Now, as the story begins, we find our sinner dead drunk, and bedded down by the side of a flea-bitten dog in the shadow of the walls of a run-down cantina. Juan could not sleep well. He saw rats everywhere—rats of all colors, *unas pintas y otras pardas*. He remembered the counsel of his friend and began to weep and then to laugh. He became aware of his bedmate and laughed louder.

"Yes," he said, "*mi vida es muy mía. Y qué!*"

A sad violin from somewhere in the dim distance began musing, in fond memory of better days when men were men.

"What is life?" asked Juan, as he noted the behavior of seven flies that had come to rest on the back of his hand.

"Listen, *moscas*, I ask you, since you get around, What is life? What? No answer? I'll show you what it is by what it isn't. *Zas!* Now you are seven dead flies, see, and I . . . I am alive and a hero."

Then Juan, moved by a festive impulse, took from his shirt pocket a small pencil and a piece of paper and wrote the following legend:

Don Juan Zurumbete
Que de un moquete
Mató siete.

And this he stuck on the crown of his sombrero and went to sleep.

He was not long asleep when one of the king's emissaries happened by the cantina and saw the stranger and the legend on the sombrero.

"How curious!" he said. "How curious! And perhaps he is what the paper says. This could be an unusual man, for there are few since the days of Bernardo del Carpio who with one blow can kill seven. Yes, my king must know about this. We need such a hero to fight the Moors for us. I shall go tell him that I have found a champion in this cantina who calls himself Don Juan Zurumbete and who, with one stroke of the hand, killed seven men."

Soon the emissary stood before the king and related his discovery.

"Fool!" said the king. "Why return to me without this warrior? Go immediately and get him. We can use such a man in our war with the Moors."

The emissary went immediately to the cantina and woke Don Juan Zurumbete.

"Get up!" he commanded. "Get up, and come with me to the king."

"And what if I don't want to speak to the king?" asked Juan. "If he wants to speak to me, *ésta es su casa.*"

The emissary was amazed at such audacity but dared not say another word, for was this not

> *Don Juan Zurumbete*
> *Que de un moquete*
> *Mató siete?*

He returned to His Majesty.

"Where is our man?" asked the king. "Why did you return without him?"

"Because, Your Majesty, I dared not try to compel a man who has killed seven with one blow of the hand," said the emissary. "It seems, Your Majesty, that this is a situation demanding discretion. Would it not be wiser to deviate some milder means for bringing him to your castle?"

The king was impressed. "Yes, you may be right," said he. "Go tell him I invite him to a banquet."

The emissary brought this message to Juan.

"Why does he want me at his banquet?" asked Juan.

"Because we know who you are," answered the emissary. "We know you are a great warrior who has killed seven men with one stroke of the hand. If that is not true, then why the legend on your hat?"

Juan laughed and was about to explain, when suddenly he decided to play along with the king's wish.

Juan met the king and said that indeed he had once killed seven with one stroke of the hand.

"That is the reason we hold you in high esteem," said the king. "We are at war with the Moors and are now, because of the death of my son, at the point of defeat. You are our last hope. If you will serve me faithfully and successfully, I shall give you my daughter in marriage."

Juan, a coward by nature, decided to admit the deception he had practiced. But again, he was prompted to accept the role of hero.

"There is nothing to do," he told himself, "but entrust myself to fate. If by chance I have an early opportunity to leave this kingdom, I shall go."

Don Juan Zurumbete was dined, feted, and wined, and on the following morning he was placed astride the famous war-horse of the dead prince. Hardly was he in the stirrups before the horse was off toward the rising sun.

Now just a few days before the king's only son had been slain by the Moors, and this famous horse was burning to avenge the death of his master. There was no steed in the whole kingdom that knew more ways of killing the enemy than he.

Miles flew by, and presently Don Juan saw a lazy smoke in a valley below.

"The Moors!" he thought. "*Madre mía*, now what am I to do?"

The Moors had mounted for their morning drill when they saw the lone horseman coming with furious speed from the west. They had never seen such daring, and they turned to flee. One by one they were run down by the famous horse and killed.

Great was the reception at the castle. Don Juan Zurumbete was not only a hero who had killed seven men with one stroke of the hand, but now the kingdom's champion who had run down and slain a whole army of Moors.

In the meantime, Don Juan had seen the princess. She was more beautiful than the sun, moon, and stars. Although completely lacking in moral fortitude, he could not refrain from asking for her hand in marriage. The king, however, had begun to suspect that Don Juan was an imposter. Yet he could not resist the fact that he was

> *Don Juan Zurumbete*
> *Que de un moquete*
> *Mató siete,*

and who had annihilated the Moors, his enemies. He made excuses for postponing the marriage and devised a scheme for the riddance of Don Juan.

It seemed, according to the king, that for some years two giants had been terrorizing the land. Don Juan was assigned the task of killing them.

"*Válgame Dios,*" he said, "is there to be no end to my troubles? True, a horse saved me from the Moors, but only fate can help me now."

He mounted his famous horse and rode away. After some days he came to the region of the giants. Don Juan had dismounted to cinch his saddle when one of the mountain men came upon him. The horse broke for safety. Don Juan took to timber and crawled into a hollow tree. The giants roared about in search of their prey. At last they found him, and feeling he would be better eating roasted, they pulled up the tree by its roots and proceeded to carry it on their shoulders to their camp.

It was now very dark. Don Juan in desperation decided on aggression. He crawled along the log which was being carried on the shoulders of the two giants as they trailed through the forest. When he reached the one in the lead, he hit him on the ear with his fist.

Turning, the offended giant yelled: "Why are you hitting me, fool? I have the heavier end to carry. Attend to your end of the trunk and let me be!"

Then, turning toward the other end, Don Juan struck the second monster on the ear.

"So you want to fight!" yelled this monster. "Well, let me tell you something. You are a coward and a liar!"

After a bit Don Juan, having as before proceeded along the trunk to the leader, struck him a blow with a dead limb.

"This is too much!" said the giant. "*Ahora verás!*"

They threw their load to the ground and fought until they had torn each other to small bits.

Don Juan gathered up four ears from the ground and returned to the king's castle.

"There is one other request I have to make," said the king. "A monstrous serpent has been killing shepherds and their flocks in a valley of my kingdom. Kill this monster and you may marry my daughter. This I promise by my word as king."

No sooner was Don Juan Zurumbete in the valley of the serpent than the latter spied him and gave chase. Don Juan lit out for the mountains with the speed of the wind, and went scrambling up a peak. He climbed with such desperation that he set the boulders rolling. One of these, a large one, headed straight for the serpent. It landed in the monster's mouth, killed him, and rolled with him into the valley below.

Don Juan, after gathering his wits, climbed down the peak, picked up a serpent fang as long as a man's arm, and made his way back to the castle.

The people hailed him as the greatest hero of all ages. He married the king's daughter and built himself a castle larger than that of the king. And the latter was afraid to do anything about it, for wasn't his son-in-law

Don Juan Zurumbete
Que de un moquete
Mató siete?

WHY WOMEN ARE LIKE CATS

I SHALL NEVER FORGET MY UNCLE Aurelio. He was a little old man whose age was well on the worse side of that of the world—which is to say, somewhat beyond fifty. His weakness was women. Now don't get me wrong. *Mi tío's* deportment was always in the clear. His only sin was an indolent levity in the presence of the ladies.

I remember one morning when some *comadres* of the hacienda were having a gabfest in the kitchen of doña Cuca.

"*Buenos días,*" said a shadow in the doorway.

"Come in, *tío* Aurelio," said doña Cuca.

And that did it. The fox was in the henhouse, so to speak, and one could not hear himself think for the screams and loud laughter.

And presently there was an argument. There was always conflict when *mi tío* mixed with the *comadres*. It is said that he loved to pick a fight with the ladies. For instance, if one should say black is black, *mi tío* would say, "*Según y conforme*—it all depends."

Upon this particular occasion the bone of contention was the superiority of men over women.

"Why should men be superior?" asked doña Paula, who, because of her stubbornness and general knowledge was known as *La Cabezona*. "Hasn't it been said that God was more skillful when he made woman? And aren't we poor little *hembras* a chip off the block of man? Doesn't the Holy Bible say that Eve was made from a rib of Adam?"

"*Según y conforme*," said *mi tío*. "I don't go for silly sayings and fairy stories."

"How scandalous, *tío*," said doña Cuca, all aghast. "Don't you believe in . . . ?"

"I do believe," said *mi tío*, "but also, with scientific certainty, I know a few things."

"*Vamos*," said someone. "Let's listen to a *sábelo todo* and God's masterpiece, ha, ha! You should have seen *mi tío* the other morning when he got his legs tangled in the pig's rope. What poise! And what dignity! There he was on the ground. At one end of the *soga* was the hind leg of the pig. At the other end, the hind legs of *mi tío*. The pig was squealing and running in circles, and *mi tío* was rolling, kicking, and swearing. *Ay, qué barbaridad!* If Satan had heard him, he would have blushed. God's masterpiece, to say the least, was quite informal. Do you think that such an honorable man should have condemned the poor *maranito* to the realm of three thousand devils? It seems to me it would have been more fitting if he had said: 'Excuse me, señor Pig; I don't believe we have had the honor of sleeping together.'"

And there followed an uproar of mocking laughter.

"Calm yourselves, señoras," said *mi tío*, as he came up for air. "Let me give you the facts in the case of the superiority of men over women, *la pura verdad*."

"*Ándale*," said the ladies, speaking with affected interest and composure.

"Well, it is true that it had been God's intention to make Eve from the rib of Adam. Our father Adam was on the operating table, and the rib had been taken from his side. God placed it on a stand nearby, and had turned away to wash his hands when the wildcat came in.

"Let it be known, *señoras de mi alma*, that the *gato montés*, during the first days of creation, sported a long tail. He came into the operating room in search of food. You see, God had been too busy with man and had had no time to prepare *comida* for his innocent creatures. Well, God's back was turned, and the cat saw the rib. He pounced upon it and out the door he went. Goodbye ladies! God gave chase. The cat saw he was losing the race and was bustling up a tree when God grabbed his tail. There was so much momentum on the part of the cat that the tail came off.

"And now what have we? *Ahora verán las señoras.* High in the tree, crouching on a limb and snarling with Adam's rib between its teeth, was the *gato montés.* On the ground was Nuestro Señor with a cat's tail in his hand.

"Nuestro Señor is wise beyond wisdom, and furthermore has a fine sense of humor. He smiled and looked first at the rib, well out of reach in a high tree, and then at what he held in his hand.

"At last he said: 'Oh, well, a cat's tail is good enough to make a woman of.' And that, *amigas*, is why women are such cats and, consequently, inferior to men."

And then you should have heard the noise in doña Cuca's kitchen. And you should have seen the speed with which *mi tío* took off for other parts.

PROSPECTORS IN PARADISE

THIS FELLOW, PEPE PERANCEJO, WAS a prospector. According to the stories about him, he had followed all the trails from Hermosillo to Chihuahua City and as far south as Colima. He found silver around Batopilas and gold at La Lluvia de Oro. Some strikes were exceptionally good, but Pepe was never satisfied. After each discovery he would invariably sell out for a few bottles of tequila and move on.

It is said that one day he vaguely remembered some reference to a city with streets of gold. He went to a priest and was told the name of the place. The padre gave directions on how to reach heaven, and soon thereafter Pepe took off for Kingdom Come.

Imagine the surprise of St. Peter when one bright morning he saw a calloused and wayworn man with a pack, shovels, and pick on his back coming up the path toward the Pearly Gates. The saint blocked the way and said:

"I am St. Peter. I shall have to frisk you and ask you a few questions."

"*Pues, escúlqueme*," said Pepe.

"Do you have any money?"

"No, señor," was the reply.

"What is your nationality?"

"Mexicano, señor."

"On earth, what did you do for a living?"

"Prospector."

"Prospector? . . . Just one little moment, please."

St. Peter began thumbing through the pages of a large book. "Now let's see," mused the saint, "carpenter, um, um, gardener, mason, painter, um, um . . ."

He closed the book, looked at Pepe, and said: "I regret to inform you that there is no mention of prospectors in the Constitution of Heaven. By the way, what is a prospector?"

"One who seeks gold, silver, and other precious metals."

St. Peter sighed with relief. "There is nothing un-Christian about that," he said. "Come in and make yourself at home."

Pepe Perancejo did just that, and ere long he had staked out claims all over the place.

St. Peter was vexed but decided to wait and watch.

Two days later there was a mighty commotion at the Pearly Gates. A score of trailweary men with packs, picks, and shovels on their backs were requesting entrance.

"The Constitution of Heaven does not provide for prospectors," said good St. Peter.

Then why did you permit Pepe Perancejo to enter?" they asked.

Now the saying has it that St. Peter is a kind good-natured old fellow but not overly bright. He has made many blunders while in heaven's immigration service, blunders like giving Pepe Perancejo permission to enter paradise, for instance. He was now in a touchy predicament. But he didn't worry.

"Oh, well," he sighed. "Come in and make yourselves at home."

Shortly thereafter the angels of heaven sent a committee to Nuestro Señor to complain about the badly cluttered condition of the streets.

"Once they were smooth, beautiful, and clean," said the committee. "You should see them now. They are badly littered with mounds, slag heaps, and shafts everywhere. The prospectors are to blame, Señor. We request that they be banished."

"Granted," said Nuestro Señor. "Tell St. Peter to get rid of them."

"This is impossible," said St. Peter when he was approached by the committee. "I let them in, and I shall lose face if I run them away."

"That is your worry," said the committee.

And worry he did, days and days of worry. At last he hit upon a plan. He went to Pepe Perancejo with his problem and suggested a solution. The latter shook his head and said it wouldn't work.

"Prospectors are a peculiar sort," said he. "They are never satisfied with well enough, and all of them without exception have the wanderlust. This is their weakness. I believe we can arrange a trap for them, and they will take themselves away; thereby you will save face. Now this is what I would do if I were you. . . ."

The next morning a telegram from hell that had been faked by Pepe and St. Peter was read to a group of angels from a balcony.

"A gold strike in hell," said the telegram. And that was all.

The following day there was only one prospector left in heaven and that was Pepe Perancejo.

He chuckled about this for a while but not for long. He became gloomy. He no longer worked his claims.

"This is a good place," he began repeating to himself. "Placers and lodes are everywhere. It is hard to imagine a better land for prospectors. Ah, my unfortunate friends! They have been gone a long time now and not one has returned. I wonder why. Could it be that . . . Could it be that . . . Ah, that's it!" he exclaimed. "The grade of ore in hell is better."

The next morning he picked up his pick and shovel, left through the Pearly Gates, and took off at a trot down the trail toward hell.

Since then prospectors have not been permitted to enter paradise.

⤸ CÁNDIDA

JUAN AND PEDRO WERE THE SONS OF wealthy *hacendados*. And, despite the fact that one was calm and good-natured and the other constantly obsessed with conniving intentions, they were friends.

They were in the capital city of the province one evening from their respective haciendas nearby, enjoying a *paseo*. Seated on a bench facing the walks of the plaza, they watched the procession of boys and girls. Suddenly, Juan exclaimed: "Look, Pedro, at the girl in green. What a dream! I am going to make her my wife."

"You can't be serious, Juan. Don't be a *pazguato*. I know her family. Her father is as poor as a mouse," said Pedro.

"All the better reason why I should marry her," said Juan.

"Let me pick a wife for you," said Pedro. "Do you see the one in blue over there? She is pretty, and better yet, she is rich. Marry for money and in that way you won't stand to lose."

Juan refused to take his friend's advice, and within a few months he had married Cándida, the one in green.

His young wife was beautiful, and her eyes were divine. Her friends spoke of her as *muy lista* (mentally vivacious), and her parents were grateful that God had given them this one and only child, who, seemingly, had no faults at all.

Time passed, and one day, like a bolt of lightning from a clear sky, Pedro said to Juan: "Pardon what I have to tell you. I have heard that your wife is unfaithful to you."

Juan paused for a long moment, and then, measuring his words, he replied: "Pedro, if anyone else had told me that, I would have killed him. However, since you are my friend, I shall simply say that it should be your duty to produce proof."

People wondered how two young men could be so unlike in character and yet so close in friendship. Some thought that Juan, because of his supine goodness, was incapable of seeing faults. And Pedro had his faults. He was selfish and given to the exploitation of any virtue or vice in others, friends included, if he could gain a few pesos in so doing.

"Juan, I have no proof at this time that Cándida is unfaithful; but I shall bet my all against all that is yours that I can get proof. Will you bet?"

"For two reasons, no," said Juan. "The first of these is that I know my wife is faithful; and the second, some things are too sacred to be used as a pawn in a game of chance."

"The first of your reasons proves you don't know women, and the second shouldn't disturb your scruples since marriage is primarily a human institution and a gamble, and you have taken that gamble already," said Pedro.

"All right," said Juan, "I will take your bet. But your evidence against Cándida must be convincing."

Pedro went immediately in search of an old *trota conventos* (woman matchmaker) whose services he had used in his philanderings.

"*Oiga*, Zorra," he said to her. "Would you like to possess a home of your own and ten *talegas* [5,000 pesos] in coin?"

La Zorra was too startled to answer. Pedro proceeded to explain the nature of his bet with Juan, and added, "I know no one can match you in cunning, and for that reason you can get the evidence I need to win this fortune."

The next day La Zorra went to see Cándida at a time when Juan was not at home. She said that she had had no food for days, and would the good señora give her a bite to eat and a few little bits of money—*una caridad*—for God's sake.

Cándida knew the meaning of poverty, and not only did she give her money but invited her into the house for food and rest.

Then La Zorra pretended to faint. Cándida called her servants, who carried the old *mendiga* to a bed in a back room and laid her down.

"Go on about your work," said Cándida to the servants. "I shall watch over her."

She lay down on a couch near the bed where La Zorra had been placed. After observing the old woman for some time, Cándida went to sleep. Then, La Zorra, cautiously opening an eye, realized the time was ripe for action. She took a small bottle from the folds of her shawl. In this bottle were dozens of *corrucos* (*piojos*, lice) she had caught and placed there for this evil purpose. She emptied the bottle on Cándida and waited. Presently the latter awoke and called a servant.

"Why do you call a servant?" asked La Zorra. "I am all right now. May I help you?"

"I am itching all over," said Cándida. "I want a change of clothes and a bath."

"I will prepare a bath while you undress," said the *mendiga*.

Cándida was undressed and reaching for a robe when the old woman returned suddenly. It was then the latter saw a black mole on the young woman's right thigh.

"I am feeling much relieved now, señora," said the *trota conventos*. "With your permission, I shall hurry home and prepare food for my grandson. *Adiós*; you have made me very happy."

She went immediately, not home but to the plaza, where she found Pedro.

"*Albricias*, Pedro," she said. "I have what you need to win your bet. Now, *daca* [hand over] that deed and the ten *talegas* of *plata*."

She explained in cruel detail what had happened when she entered Cándida's home. "The black mole couldn't have been placed more to our advantage," she said, giggling.

It took a few days of cautious maneuvering to arrange a deed for the *mendiga* and to get the money he promised her. After that he went to Juan and said: "*Amigo*, I don't know how to tell you this except to say that bread is bread and wine is wine. In short, to put it bluntly, you have lost the bet." He told the unhappy young man about the black mole.

"*Ya todo se acabó* [that's the end of everything]," said Juan as he left in a stupor.

The young husband didn't go home that night. The next morning he had his *mayordomo* saddle two horses and leave them hitched to a post near the big house. He then went to Cándida and explained that he had urgent business in a city two days' ride from the hacienda, and that it was his desire that she accompany him.

After having traveled in a mountain wilderness for hours, he suggested they rest for awhile. He dismounted and helped his wife from her horse. Then, quickly, he swung into his saddle and, catching the reins of the other animal, hurried away, leaving her to die of starvation.

Cándida, after days of wandering and with her last bit of energy, dragged herself to a small house near a river. She was without shoes, her clothes were torn to tatters, and her face was the picture of agony. An old woman helped her into the house and put her to bed.

It was while working in a small garden near the old woman's home some days later that Cándida sensed that someone, somewhere, was spying on her. She looked about and saw an Indian standing still like a post not thirty feet away. Indians had come to her hacienda often and she was not afraid of them. Yet, this old man did not come to her to ask for *ni-the-mua* (tobacco) or *escupua-a-pua* (salt). He stood there and stared with an expressionless face. Suddenly, he turned and ran into the brush.

That afternoon horsemen surrounded the little home of the kind old *nana* (grandmother). Among them was Juan de Miranda, Cándida's husband.

"Cándida, Cándida, at last we have found you, thanks to God and this Indian tracker. Yes, my wife, it was all a horrible nightmare, something I should like to forget. But let me tell you now that an old *mendiga*, claiming that Pedro was cheating her, stabbed him; and before he died he confessed the whole dirty business to me. The old woman is in custody. Come, let's go home. I shall have to spend the rest of my life praying for your forgiveness."

"This old *nana* here saved my life, Juan. Let's see to it that her years end happily."

"Your wish is mine," said Juan.

JOVITA AND MANUELITO

ERA QUE ERA, AND ONCE UPON A TIME there was a wealthy family that lived in a land far away. Strange though it may seem, in addition to the man, his wife, and his young daughter, there was only one servant who had been reared a *criado* with the girl.

And there came a time when the father and mother of the family died. Thus it was that Jovita, the daughter, and Manuelito, the servant, were left alone in the world.

One day Jovita said to Manuelito: "Now what are we going to do? My father and mother are dead."

Then she said impulsively: "You know what? I shall have my picture taken and many copies made, and I shall have them sent out over the world to see if someone might be interested in me."

Time passed and there was no reply to her pictures. One day

she said to Manuelito: "Now let's try something else. Would you like to make a bargain with me? Manuelito, let's you and me get married."

"Oh, no," said Manuelito. "Remember those pictures. Some day someone would take you away from me."

"No, no," said Jovita. "Nothing like that will happen."

Then Manuelito was willing, and they were married.

One day of so many happy days Jovita said: "Listen, Manuelito, if I should die, would you be willling to be buried alive with me?"

"Yes; why not?" he said.

"And how would I know that you would fulfill this promise? Let us sign a compact with the blood of our bodies. We shall say: Whoever remains after the death of one of us will be buried alive together with the one who died. And so? Are you willing?"

"Yes; why not?" he said.

At last a time arrived when Jovita died. And Manuelito complied with his promise. He had a mason build a large vault, and he followed his beloved dead into the tomb. He arranged that a keeper of the dead should bring him food every day.

One day as he sat eating beside the coffin of his wife he noticed a small mouse that was busy gathering the crumbs that fell at his feet. And this small mouse became a companion. Once he observed that the mouse had brought a small flower into the vault as a plaything. He was amused; he picked up a pebble and thoughtlessly tossed it toward the *animalito. Ay, Dios*; he should not have done that! The pebble hit his little friend and killed it.

Not knowing what he was about to do, he took the flower and placed it at the nose of the mouse. The latter sprang to its feet and ran away.

"I wonder," said Manuelito. "Could this small white flower be *La Flor de la Vida?*"

And then he opened the coffin at his side and said: "Jovita, my little mouse came alive. Oh, to Allah and to God that you too may now return from the dead. Look, what a beautiful flower!"

He passed the flower beneath her nose, and her lips began to move. He continued in his prayer to God until she was awake. He made no mention of where they were.

Then she said, "Where are we?"

"We are here in a tavern," he replied. "A gentleman looks after our interests."

At that instant the guardian of the dead came to the vault.

"With whom are you talking, Manuelito?" he asked.

"I am speaking with Jovita."

And then, with a look of pity on his face, the guardian asked, "Do you wish for something to eat?"

"No," replied Manuelito. "I want you to open the door of this vault and leave it open."

The guardian refused.

"If you will leave the door open," said Manuelito, "I will give you certain riches that I have hid in my house. Here, these are the keys to the house. Go, see for yourself."

That night the two, Jovita and Manuelito, left the tomb. They walked through the dark until they came to an inn. Here they asked for lodging.

Days passed and Manuelito was taken to bed with a fever.

Some girls came to the inn one afternoon and asked if Jovita would accompany them to the shore. "A foreign king in a large ship is coming to visit," they said.

And though he felt no good would come from their request, Manuelito consented and Jovita left him there, alone and ill.

The king in all his splendor stood on the deck of his ship with a picture in his hands. He looked at this picture and at the girls on the shore.

There was no delay. Jovita was carried away.

The girls who had accompanied Jovita to the dock returned to Manuelito's room. "We are unhappy, Manuelito. They have taken your wife away."

Manuelito was very sad. However, within a few days he was on his feet again. He walked along the beach and learned that the king who had stolen his wife had given an order that no one, under penalty of death, was to follow him across the sea.

Manuelito returned to his room and began to tear and repatch some of his clothes. He now looked like a beggar or a very poor man. He bribed a friend to close him in a barrel and roll him into the sea.

Ere long he was in a foreign land. He pretended to be looking

for work, but he knew well the object of his search. He arrived at
the home of an old woman who had a son who was employed in the
palace of the king.

"Look, son, this young man wants work at the palace. Tell the
king that he is your brother who has lived down the coast for some
time."

"What is your name?" asked the young man.

"My name," said Manuelito, "my name is Juan Soldadillo."

The young man went into the presence of the king and said,
"I have with me a young man."

"Yes?" responded the king. "Where are you from?"

"I am a relative of your servant here. I am his brother and
have been living down the coast for a bit. My name is Juan Soldadillo."

"Do you want work?" asked the king.

"Yes, Your Majesty; I am at your command," said Manuelito.

This Manuelito, who was now known as Juan Soldadillo, was
given work in the kitchen. He went about his chores in a dull way
with a large hat pulled down over his eyes.

Once, while the queen was inspecting the kitchen, she noticed
the new servant.

"What is your name?" she asked.

"*Pos*, Juan Soldadillo," he drawled.

The queen was curious and continued to visit the kitchen day
by day. There was something about this servant that reminded her
of her husband. And before long and after asking many questions,
she discovered that indeed Juan Soldadillo was her husband
Manuelito.

Ere long the king noticed that the queen was upset and badly
disturbed. "Listen, my queen," he said, "why are you sad?"

"Why shouldn't I be sad," she replied, "since the one we have
serving as kitchen sweeper is my husband?"

"Ah," said the king. "So; *qué bueno!* This is fine, yes, very fine."

Later the king, very angry, called Manuelito into his presence
and said: "Juan Soldadillo, tonight you are to guard three ounces
of my gold. If any of it is lost I shall have you executed."

The king tricked Manuelito by having two other servants steal
the gold. Manuelito rushed to his pseudobrother and said:

"After I am executed you are to claim my body. Watch over it throughout the night. Then get a horse, the most *ladino* of those in the king's stable. Hitch this horse to a hack. Look; I want you to listen well to this that I have to say. I have a flower. At four o'clock in the morning you are to pass this flower back and forth beneath my nose and petition God that I be returned to life. After I have been revived and have departed, go to the door of the king's room and shout, 'All the devils of hell have taken Juan Soldadillo away!' "

On the morning of the execution the king said to his queen, Jovita, "Come and watch the execution of your husband."

After the execution the friend did all that he had promised Manuelito to do. After the resuscitation he saw to it that his friend should be spirited away to another city. This city was in mourning over the death of the favorite daughter of the emperor.

Manuelito went to the palace of the emperor and asked, "Your Majesty, what will you give me to return your daughter to life?"

"With the death of a certain king I shall name, I shall restore your daughter to life," said Manuelito.

"Be it as you request," said the emperor. "The only thing I ask is the life of my daughter."

Manuelito went to the dead princess, passed the flower back and forth beneath her nose, and prayed to God. The girl awoke. The emperor was amazed. He ordered the execution of the king immediately.

Just before the death of the king, Manuelito said to Jovita, "Come and see the execution of your husband."

Manuelito and Jovita are still in this world and are living together happily.

Chapter Seven

⤙ JULIO

JULIO WAS AN ORPHAN. HIS FATHER was a poor man, one of *los de abajo*. All he possessed when death came upon him was twenty pesos. This money was left to Julio. After the funeral the latter said:

"I have no father. I have no mother. This silver is the only thing I possess. Now that there is nothng to keep me here, I shall wander. I can't wait around for whatever future there is in life for me."

He took to the road. After much uneventful and aimless trekking, he encountered two individuals, and one said to him, "Where goest thou, young man?"

And Julio responded, "Señores, let it be known to you that I travel the trail of life in search of my destiny."

The stranger replied: "Very well and good; yet, on the other hand, it isn't so good and well, for you have chosen a path that has led you to the secret hideout of a gang of thieves. Right here and now your travels have ended, as they have for all who tried to pass this way."

Julio said: "Señores, don't kill me. All that I can give you are twenty pesos my father left me when he died. You may have them, but please spare my life."

"Well," said one of the robbers, "hand over the money and move on. However, I warn you. Tell no one what has happened here; otherwise we will follow and kill you."

After leagues of further wandering Julio came on the body of a young man that lay beside the path.

Then Julio mused: "Poor chap, he wasn't so fortunate as I. His only need now is a grave."

Julio worked hard with only a sharp stick for a spade. He placed the body in a shallow trench and covered it with dirt and the leaves of a prickly pear.

Soon after this, as he rested beside the road, he saw a young man approaching.

"*Para donde?* [where are you going?]" asked the stranger.

"Just seeking adventure," said Julio.

"My name is Antonio," said the young man. "You are Julio, if I remember well. Shall we travel together?"

After five days of walking, they came to a city. Neither had so much as a centavo.

"Now we shall enter an inn," said Antonio. "We need rest and food."

"And with no money?" asked Julio. "How long would we stay there, and what would we eat without *plata?*"

"Leave that to me," said Antonio. "Listen; tonight we shall have money."

"Well, all right," said Julio. "You lead the way."

"No, upon second thought," said Antonio, "I shall go to the inn, and you run down to the municipal palace and ask for permission to give a play tonight. After you get the permit, look for a place where this drama can be presented."

Julio went immediately to the *presidencia* and greeted the alcalde.

"How may we serve you?" asked the latter.

Julio gave a *pagaré* (an IOU) for the official document. The price was three pesos.

Then he went in search of a corral, and after an hour or so he found what he wanted. He gave the proprietor of the place his *pagaré* for five pesos. Thereupon he went to the inn to report to Antonio.

"Now," said Antonio, "go and find us some music. We shall need the best orchestra available."

A violinist in a saloon told Julio where he could get an orchestra. He presented himself to the conductor and they came to terms. Julio gave this man his *pagaré* for twenty pesos. Julio told him to put up a front of music at the corral beginning at seven o'clock that evening.

"Make all the pleasant music you can," said Julio. "We want a large attendance."

He felt that luck had been with him up to this point, yet he began to have a few doubts about Antonio. "How did he know my name when we first met on the road?" he thought. "Furthermore, if this wild dream about a drama comes to naught, who will pay the twenty-eight pesos I owe in *pagarés*? And who is to give this *comedia*? For my part, I don't know a jot about acting. *Quién sabe?* I shall speak to Antonio about this."

He was almost breathless from haste and worry when he encountered Antonio.

"*Amigo mío,*" he blurted out. "Where are the actors for our *comedia?*"

"They are awaiting us at the corral," said Antonio.

By eight o'clock the corral was full to overflowing with people eager to see the show. Antonio and an actress presented the first *auto*. Then Julio and a younger girl gave the second. It seemed as though he recited by magic. What beautiful words! What charming sentiments!

Then a third *auto* was given, and Antonio rose and thanked the crowd for the favorable reception. "Now, my amiable *audiencia,*" he continued, "señoras and señores, this orchestra is yours until dawn. Dance and be happy, for no one knows what tomorrow will bring."

The following morning Julio paid his debts, and he and Antonio left the city.

After two weeks of travel they came to the foot of a high mountain. They climbed to the top and paused on a peak.

"Julio," said Antonio, "from here we see the world. With our money and with directions wherever one looks, what else is there to wish for? Where shall we go from here?"

"*Pues, no le hace,*" said Julio. "Wherever you say is all right with me."

"Thanks for your confidence," said Antonio. "However, Julio, don't you think you are a bit too trusting? Don't be too innocent, *amigo.*"

After they had descended halfway down the peak Antonio stopped suddenly and said, "Do you see that large house at the base of the canyon?"

"That is no house," said Julio. "It is only a canyon wall in many colors."

"Yes," said Antonio, disregarding the words of Julio, "it is not only a large house but a city of houses. Let's spend the night there."

"*Pues, está bueno,*" shrugged Julio, "but we shall be lucky to find a cave in which to sleep."

"Look, *amigo,*" said Antonio. "Man is endowed with sight, some more, some less. There are those who see with the eyes of animals, and others can glimpse the supernatural. Wake up, *amigo,* and clear your eyes; for we are soon to enter an enchanted city. Faith, *amigo*; faith! Already I see the king's castle. And, by the way, there is some writing on the door, and this writing says, 'My daughter the princess shall marry the man who can read her thoughts.' Go, Julio, and see this *rétulo* for yourself, and tell the king that you will guess the thoughts of his daughter."

With a world of misgivings Julio descended into the canyon and to his amazement found himself reading the inscription on the castle door.

"Why are you here, young man?" asked the king.

"I," said Julio, "I have come to explore the mind of the princess, Your Majesty."

"My young friend," said the king, "that has never been done since the day of the tragic enchantment ages ago. Be it known to you that a wicked sorcerer holds my daughter and my city in a spell. However, if you wish to try your luck you may do so; but mind you, the price of failure is death."

"I shall read your daughter's thoughts," said Julio. "*Hasta mañana.* I shall return then."

That night the sorcerer spoke with the princess and said: "To-morrow a young man will come to tell you what you think. Remember, you are to meditate upon yourself, then ask him, 'Can you guess my thoughts?' "

In the meantime Antonio had said to Julio: "When the king's daughter asks you to reveal her thoughts, you are to say: 'You think about yourself,' and then without another word you are to return to me, for that *mal genio* is going to demand two more trials, and we want to be prepared for him. He is a sly one, *muy ladino*, and I don't trust him. Tomorrow, the second time you are tested, you are to say, 'You think about your shoes.' "

"And the day after that?" asked Julio.

"*Poco a poco,*" said Antonio. "I am preparing a surprise for this *mágico poderoso.*"

The second test was as easy as the first; and Julio, without so much as a courteous farewell, returned to Antonio.

The third day Julio faced the princess with a sack containing the head of the *genio*. "You were told," said Julio, "to concentrate upon the head of the sorcerer. Here is his head."

The king was overjoyed at Julio's success. He said to him, "To-night, my son, you shall sleep here in my castle."

In this enchanted city there had been no sounds for ages. Julio had heard nothing further than the words of the princess and her father. That night, however, while in a dull half-sleep he awoke to the distant tolling of a bell. This was followed by the dismal wail of a dog. And then burros and roosters began braying and crowing. Now a *sereno* called out, "*Ave María purísima, son las doce y todo sereno* [twelve o'clock and all is well]." Thereupon, people began shouting, "*Viva la vida!*" There were parades and marching of soldiers and bands on the streets. With unrestrained emotion the people were shouting again and again, "*Viva la vida! Viva la vida!*"

At dawn the streets were silent again. The inhabitants of the city walked about as if in a dream.

"Julio," said Antonio, "we have more to do. Go now to the king and tell him you want his daughter in marriage. He will consent, for that was a condition of the *rétulo*. But, first, you must insist on taking a walk with the girl. Take her to the lagoon in the brush near the outskirts of the city and tell her to strip and bathe. She will refuse, and then you are to whip her with a willow switch. Hit her hard and force her into the water. When she leaves the lagoon a young mare will come to the bank for water. Whip this filly into the lagoon. When she leaves a dove will settle upon a branch near you. Catch this dove and whip it into the lagoon as you did with the princess and the mare. After this your marriage will be a happy one, for your wife will obey you. She will not be giddy and wild, and best of all, she will not go about sighing. Now, my friend Julio, *adiós*."

"No," said Julio, "you are not leaving. I shall provide for you in my castle."

"*Amigo*, you must be a bit more *desconfiado*. You don't know me," said Antonio. "I was in your home twice, and there I learned your name."

"But I had never seen you before our chance meeting upon a path three weeks ago."

"Do you remember the body you buried the morning before we met? I am that body. I am Death."

With this, Death departed. Julio bathed his princess, the mare, and the dove in the lagoon. For years and years he and his queen had lived happily. Indeed, there is no recorded history that Death ever came again to the disenchanted city.

ᔈ JUAN AND THE BONY ONE

THIS WAS A TIME OF SCARCITY IN A land far away, many years ago. A mother called her three sons and said to them:

"My sons, as you well know, times are hard. We must have food, and that means one of you must seek work."

The oldest boy, a vain and presumptuous young man, said: "Mother, we must think of our honor. But since you suggest it, I shall leave for some distant land where I am not known and get a job."

After much travel this young man came to the castle of a king and was enlisted to help guard the palace. Weeks and months passed and he sent no word to his family.

Now, with only three mouths to feed instead of four, the family should have fared better; but food was scarce. For breakfast there was for each a cup of *atole* made by grinding up old tortillas and mesquite beans. At noon the meal consisted of one tortilla and a small serving of beans for each. And for supper, when there was anything at all to eat, it was a tortilla.

One day the second son left home, presumably in search of work. He, too, by chance, went to the king's palace and was hired as a page. He did not write home to tell the mother that he had found his brother and that each had a job.

Finally the mother said to Juan, her youngest son: "Juanito, you are now a big boy. I want you to go in search of your brothers. I fear they have come to harm in some land far away."

Thus it was that Juan asked for the blessing of his mother and departed. After much wandering, he, too, came to the castle of the king and was placed in the stables as a *caballerango*. And by pure chance he met his brothers. The latter were displeased that he had taken employment as a stableboy. An argument followed, and one of the two said to him: "We are ashamed of you. If people here learn that you are our brother, we shall see to it that the king sends you home."

Juan was a good boy and wept at their insults. But also, Juan was a stubborn boy and refused to quit his job.

The king had a *remuda* of fine horses, and Juan fed and brushed them daily. One of these horses, though, had been losing weight.

"Juanito," said His Majesty, "this horse has been the best in my stables, but now he is nothing but skin and bones. Also, he has begun to balk and lie down whenever he is saddled. I will give my daughter in marriage to anyone who can cure him."

It was about this time that the queen died, and the king forthwith issued a *bando* in which he asked that some brave man cross the waters of the sea and bring back a beautiful princess who lived there.

"I must have a queen immediately," he said.

The older brothers, that is to say, the page and the guard, read this *bando* and plotted to destroy Juan. They went to the king and told him that Juanito had boasted that he could fetch the princess.

"Juanito," said His Majesty, "I was told that you have been bragging about how easy it would be to cross the sea and bring the princess to us."

"No, Your Majesty, I have said nothing of the sort."

"All the same, Juanito, you are going to make good your boast, or I shall see to it that you are hanged as a stupid fool. Think it over and give me your answer in three days. I like you, my boy, and would hate to see you hanged."

Juan returned to the stable, his face all *pucheritos* and a sea of tears.

"What's wrong?" asked the poor horse, who by now had taken a liking to Juan.

"No, nothing," said Juan, "only that the king has threatened my life if I don't bring him a princess from abroad."

"Don't worry," said the horse, who now was known as the Bony One. "We shall manage to carry out his command."

On the third day Juan went to the king and agreed to go over the sea for the princess.

"How much money will you need?" asked the king.

"I will need no money. Arrange that food be prepared for me and grain for my mount, and I shall leave immediately," said Juan.

The following morning the king and his noblemen were at the corral when Juan saddled for his journey.

"You fool!" shouted His Majesty. "Why ride the Bony One? Get the boy a good horse. On that *penco* he will go perhaps a league, and then the *mañoso* will balk and lie down."

"Either I ride this horse or I refuse to go," said Juan.

At midday he came to a small meadow in the mountains, and in the very center of this meadow was a tall pine, and high in the tree sat a bird, singing.

"We shall rest here," said the Bony One, "and by the way, as we eat, feed that bird. He may fit into our plans later."

The bird ate and said, "If you should ever need me, just call out, '*Aquí de mi pajarito*.'"

The horse and his rider spent the night near the sea. At dawn a fish came to the shore. The horse said that it should be fed.

"He may fit into our plans later," he said.

After the fish had eaten it breathed bubbles through the water and said, "Should you ever need me, just call, '*Aquí de mi pescadito*.'"

"We should be on our way," said the Bony One. "Mount now, blindfold yourself, lift the reins, and we shall cross the sea."

When they reached the distant shore the horse had changed to
a high-spirited animal of seven colors. They proceeded to the plaza
of a large city. "Now, Juan, we shall do a *vuelta* around the square
so the princess can see us. Straighten your back and ride with pride.
Leave the rest to me."

The princess saw them and asked her father if she might ride
the beautiful horse of seven colors. The king sent for Juan and explained that the princess wanted to ride his horse a couple of
vueltas around the square. Juan said he felt greatly honored that
so beautiful a girl should want to ride his horse, but he said this
particular animal would permit no one other than himself to mount
him.

The king laughed and said: "Young man, I have *jinetes* in my
cavalry who can ride anything on four legs. You just leave the riding
to us."

He sent for a *domador*. The latter approached the horse of
seven colors and *allí fue Troya*. The horse backed his ears, bared
his teeth, and would have killed the breaker had Juan not calmed
him down.

"If it should please Your Majesty," he said, "let the princess
mount behind me."

While soldiers were taking security measures by blocking all
exits to the square, the horse of seven colors told Juan that after
they had completed the second *vuelta* with the princess, he should
then close his eyes and lift the reins.

Thus it was that the princess was kidnapped and brought to
the king who wanted to marry her. After she was informed of the
king's intentions, she said: "I lost a *tumbaga* while crossing the sea.
I shall marry no one until it is found and returned to me."

Again the brothers, motivated by their criminal hatred, devised
a new plan to destroy Juan. They went to the king and told him
that Juanito had boasted he could find the ring.

"Likely the rogue stole it on the way over," said the king. "Send
him to me."

"Juanito," said he, "I hear you have been boasting again, and
just for that, I am demanding that you, within three days, produce
a ring the princess lost while crossing the sea. If you fail, you will
be hanged."

Juan returned to the stables, and his friend, the one of seven colors, observed his sadness.

"Is the king demanding the impossible again?" asked the horse. "Don't worry; we shall manage somehow. Remember our friend the fish?"

They went to the shore and Juan called out, "*Aquí de mi pescadito.*" The fish appeared and was asked to help find the ring. And in less time than it takes to say *santiamén*, Juan held the *tumbaga* in his hand. And when it was presented to the princess, the king was overjoyed and cried out, "Now we shall marry!"

"No," said the princess. "I shall marry no one until I have been given a small flask of the Water of Life."

And again the king issued a *bando*, but no one knew where to seek the Water of Life. And again Juan's brothers sought to destroy him. The king sent for him and gave him three days to find a flask of *el Agua de la Vida.*

Juan took his sadness to the horse again. "We shall manage somehow," said the latter.

They went to the tall pine in the small meadow and Juan called, "*Aquí de mi pajarito.*" A small flask was tied to the bird's foot, and it flew away to the mountains that spent the time bumping their heads together just to make the boulders roll. Zigzagging and darting hither and thither to avoid the rolling stones, it filled the flask at the Spring of Life and returned.

"Ah," said the king, "the third time charms. Now, to be sure, we shall marry."

"Yes," said the princess, "but first, I must have permission of the *Pájaro Cú.* I shall marry no one without its consent."

Again the king issued a *bando*. And again the brothers sought to destroy Juan. The king gave the latter three days to bring the *Pájaro Cú* to the princess.

"The bird is in the land of the Moors," said the horse. "The *Paisano* and the *Tecolote* have been looking for it for ages. Mount, close your eyes, lift the reins, and we shall go fetch the fine-feathered bird. Now, when we get to the *morisma*, we shall give a few *vueltas* about the plaza. When you see the Moors with their eyes closed, beware. They see when they seem to sleep."

They went about the square until all the Moors had their eyes open. Then Juan stole the *Pájaro Cú*, golden cage and all (*con toi jaula de oro*), closed his eyes, lifted the reins, and was soon home again at the palace.

The king was in the corral when Juan returned. "Take the bird to the princess," he ordered. And then he approached the horse. "What a beautiful animal!" he said as he came near. Suddenly, the horse of seven colors wheeled and kicked the king dead.

"Now, Juan, go marry the king's daughter, for it is generally known that he promised the princess in marriage to anyone who could fatten me and cure me of balking and lying down," said the one of seven colors.

After the wedding, the foreign princess was returned across the waters of the sea to her father. A regal *bando* was issued to the effect that Juan's brothers be dragged to death by wild mules. The mother was brought to the palace to live with Juan and his queen; and the Bony One, who is no longer bony but rolling in fat, never balks and never lies down, not even while asleep.

↳ KLIS-TO E-E-KI TA-U-UE-A

I-ni, WELL, YOU KNOW IN YOUR HEART that buzzards are a slow-thinking sky-people who eat dead things. Yet, once upon a time they were lean and beautiful. It is even said that they were captains of all sky-people.

I-ni, well, that was before the time Ta-u-ue-a (buzzard) left Klis-to (Christ) hanging on the horn of the moon.

Klis-to needed blue paint for his face. He gazed at the blue of the sky and wondered how he could get there. It was then that Ta-u-ue-a came to Klis-to and they understood. Ta-u-ue-a said: "As you wish, I shall carry you to the blue of the sky."

Ka-pot-ue, then, he said: "Get up here on my back."

Ta-u-ue-a went flying away, up and up, and left Klis-to on the horn of the moon. "You wait here," he said, "while I look for something to eat. When I come back we shall return to the earth."

Ta-u-ue-a forgot to come back, and Klis-to was tired. He called over and over again: "Hey, *ne-ci-the* [my uncle], I am tired. Come and get me."

No one came and Klis-to was angry.

Klis-to said: "He doesn't come back. I have been here for ten hours and can stand this hanging and waiting no longer. I am going to let go."

He changed to a leaf and fell earthward. He prayed to God that he not fall on the ground. "Let me fall in a hollow tree," was his supplication.

And there he was in a hollow tree, waiting and wondering what to do next. He changed back to Klis-to from a leaf.

A *pá-ci-to* (little old man) and a *me-che-mo-a* (little old woman) were in the forest looking for firewood and small game. The *me-che-mo-a* carried an ax and the *pá-ci-to* a bow and arrows.

It was then the *me-che-mo-a* found the hollow tree and began to chop. Klis-to heard and wondered who made the noise. "Perhaps it is my younger brother *a-me-kua* [beaver]," he said.

"Let me out," called Klis-to. "In here I can neither go up nor down. Cut a bigger hole."

The *me-che-mo-a* was frightened. "He talks our language," she said, "and he talks Castilian. He is not an animal. He is a man."

Klis-to came from the hollow tree and spoke to them. "I wish you pleasure," he said. "You thought I was a bear in that tree. *Na-hi*, all right; I have three bears for you, a mother and two cubs. *Nu-ui-nu ma-kue-he* [come out, bear]," he said.

The *pá-ci-to*, while running this way and that behind trees and bushes, made ready with his bow and arrows. The *me-che-mo-a* climbed a tree. The animals came out, one by one, and were killed.

"I give you these," said Klis-to. "I have just arrived here from the sky. When you speak of me to the *me-to-sé-ne-ni* [Indian people], they will want proof that you saw me. Since some do not believe what their eyes can't see, I have provided you with *ma-kua* meat. That should be convincing since the bow and arrows of *pá-ci-to* are not for bear but for small game."

I-ni. Now about Ta-u-ue-a. Klis-to was still angry and wondered how he could trap and punish Ta-u-ue-a for leaving him so long on the moon.

"When I was on his back, he smelled bad," said Klis-to. "I believe he has been with dead animals."

Klis-to threw himself on the ground and changed to a dead fox. Ta-u-ue-a was flying high when he saw this animal.

"*Ku!*" he said. "Something is dead."

Ta-u-ue-a came to earth not too close to the dead fox. "I must take care," he said, "for he may be alive."

He stopped and stared with one eye and then with the other. Then, with much caution, he came closer still. He looked to the sky and all about.

The fox, now Klis-to, sprang to his feet and caught him.

"You forgot me," said Klis-to to Ta-u-ue-a. "You left me to hang ten hours on the moon. Even sky-people are punished for their faults. I shall hold you captive for ten years. Even on the day of the dance I shall hold you. I shall strip you of your honor among the sky-people, and no longer will you be known as *Ui-na-kue-e*, but simply as *Ta-u-ue-a* [buzzard]."

And this is why he is as he is.

I-ni-me-ke-kui-ke-ke-ne-ma-ki (This is as far as I know).

◟ SEEIN' SNAKES

ONE EVENING AFTER SUPPER, WHILE in Musquiz, Coahuila, Mexico, I sat at a table in a saloon working on my Kickapoo notes, when an uninvited guest showed up at my side.

"Wad chu do?" he asked.

"Oh, nothing in particular," I answered.

He leaned low over my paper, closed an eye, and studied the words. The odor of his breath was like sour sorghum. It was evident that he was a bit high on something, and that something was not water.

"*Quiere una copa de añejo?*" I asked.

"I no like tequila," he said. "I take a wheeskley. I like a dark dreenk an' a white woman. Wad chu do; you write a somethin'?"

"I am gathering folklore," I told him. "Do you know a *cuento* you would like to tell?"

"Chu wan' me tell a story, wan thaz no lie?"

"*Cuento o historia; no le hace* [A story or a bit of history; it doesn't matter]."

His eyes seemed to focus for an instant, and he said: "Chu know wan time som' boys they wanna peek feegs. The tree, he ees tall.

Wan boy, he don' know wad ees a feeg. A boy, he climb in the tree and throw feegs down an' the odder boys, they peek um op and eat um. The boy wad don' know wad ees a feeg, he ask, 'How many legs does have the feeg?' The boys say, 'The feeg no have a leg.'

" 'Hah,' say the boy who don' know wad ees a feeg. 'I chos eat wan weeth four legs.' Wad chu know! The dam fool keed, he eat a frog. Ha, ha; thas a good story, no?"

"Fine, just fine," I said, working fast with my pencil. "Let's have another."

"Mebbe so, mebbe no, chu no like a story 'bout San Isiro? Okydokie! San Isiro, he had a girl wan time. She wanna go to a peekneek, and she borrow a reeng from anodder girl. That girl she geed seek an' die. These girl, she no like to ask for reeng back from a dead girl, bot wan day she go to San Isiro an' tellum: 'San Isiro, the girl, she die I loan um reeng. I like to geed the reeng.' San Isiro, he look an' canna fin' the reeng. San Isiro he say, 'Chu wait.'

"San Isiro, he go to the grave an' pray. He ask the girl where ees the reeng, and the girl tellum from the grave where ees the reeng.

"Ah; mebbe so chu like anoder. Thees ees about . . . wad chu callum? . . . ah . . . ship man."

"A sailor," I prompted.

"No, no, ship man, ship man, wan man who goes in mountains with the ships."

"Sheep man?" I gambled.

"Yes, ship man." (Why he insisted on a short *i* instead of a long *e* sound in the word sheep, I shall never know.) "A ship man an' a nun . . . no . . . a man . . . wad chu callum, San Isiro, wad chu callum . . . ah, a monk, thaz wad, a monk, San Isiro.

"The ship man, he work out. San Isiro, he paz that way. He say, 'Wad chu doin'?' The ship man, he say: 'I make a leevin' for the keeds. I heet on the rocks, break um op, sell um, make money.'

"A snake, she ron by. San Isiro peek um op, and she is torn [turned to] gol'. 'Take a snake to three ball shop, an' the *gachupín*, he geeve chu some leetle money,' say San Isiro.

"The ship man, he tak' a snake waz now gol'. The *gachupín*, he see the snake, she is all gol'. When ship man wanna leetle money, the *gachupín* sholers [shoulders] they go op. He's glad to geeve leetle money for gol' snake.

"Later, the ship man, he go to getta snake and the *gachupín*, he say: 'No gottum. Somebody stealum. She's gone.'

"Ship man, he go back to San Isiro. San Isiro, he tellum, 'Chu go anoder time.' Ship man, he go anoder time. And the *gachupín*, he say: 'No gottum snake. She get away.' Ship man, he go to San Isiro anoder time. San Isiro, he say: 'Chu go thir' time. Tellum chu chos wanna see snake, an' not to takeum, chos to see um.'

"The *gachupín*, he open box where ees the snake, an' the snake no longer gol'. She's chos snake."

"*Que cuento tan curioso* [what a curious story]," I said.

"Thaz no *cuento*," said my tipsy friend. "Thaz no lie. I see um weeth the two eyes."

⤸ DESTINY

TWO BROTHERS, JUAN AND PEDRO, HAD inherited the family *granja*. This was a good farm, very fertile and well located with regard to market and water; but it was small.

"Our homestead," said the father before he died, "is large enough for both of you if you will work it together. Whatever you do don't divide it."

But Juan, a dreamer, wasn't satisfied. "It is not right that I get as much of this land as Pedro," he said. "I, a *soltero*, need little while Pedro with his large family needs much. I shall never feel right about this, and there is only one thing to be done—I shall sell my part and leave."

Pedro, with his good heart and level head, tried to dissuade Juan from his purpose; but for all his goodness he got nowhere. Pedro paid him cash for his interest in the farm, and Juan left the old homestead.

Within a few years he had lost all his money in wild investments and get-rich-quick schemes. Then he was forced to work at odd jobs. He did not complain until he began pondering over the big problem of *mine* and *thine*. "Destiny," he said, "destiny has dealt badly with me; yet I deserve what I have come by. My brother said once that gold was to be had from the soil of the *granja* and that 'a *veces el oro no resplandece* [sometimes gold doesn't glisten].' I wonder how it goes with Pedro now."

He wandered back toward the family farm. Eventually, he came to a large wheat field. He asked a passerby who owned it and was told that a certain señor Tal para Cual was the proprietor. Later he saw a beautiful orchard, and still later a rich vineyard. These too, he was informed, were owned by the same señor Tal para Cual, who was none other than Pedro himself. Juan became bitter—not against Pedro, but against his own *mala suerte* (bad luck, fate).

"I have tried, *según mis miras*, to make a go of life," he complained. "Something somewhere is wrong, and I can't get my hands on it to correct it."

Just then he spied a beautiful old woman seated beneath an arbor. "Who owns this?" he asked.

"It belongs to your brother Pedro," answered the woman.

"How does it happen that you know me?" he asked.

"For the simple reason that I am your brother's *suerte*."

"*Dispénseme*, but will you tell me how I am to find the one who holds my fortune in her hand?"

"Seek and thou shalt find," she said.

Feeling somewhat relieved, Juan went to his brother's house. Here he was welcomed as a prodigal. He was fed and clothed and asked to make the *granja* his home. However, he was intent on finding his *suerte*; and one morning, at early dawn, he set out on his search.

He hadn't proceeded far when he came upon an old hag near a gutter. She was asleep and seemed the worse off for drink. He nudged her awake with his foot and asked, "Who are you?"

"I am your *suerte*," she said. "You can thank my long siesta for those fine clothes you wear. If I had been awake you wouldn't have them."

"Do you hate me as much as all that?" he asked.

"Don't blame me. You should speak to El Destino [Destiny]."

"How do I find El Destino?"

She directed him to a hermit who lived in a cave some leagues away. This old man referred him to one older yet; and the latter, in turn, sent him farther into the mountains to the oldest hermit in the land.

"I have come to ask you the directions to El Destino," said Juan.

"Young man, I have lived in these parts for a mighty long time, and I'm sorry that I can't help you. Yet, I rule the birds of the air; and if you will wait until sunup, I'll call them in. Perhaps one of them knows about this El Destino," said the third and oldest hermit.

At dawn the following morning this old man with the long white beard whistled three times; and the birds of the air, all except one, came to him. He whistled again and again. Far on the distant horizon they saw an eagle. At last he lit near his master and said: "I heard you call, but I was attending a festival given by El Destino. I regret my delay."

"Very well," said the hermit. "Take this man on your back and return to El Destino."

When Juan and the eagle reached the home of Destiny, the bird said: "When you enter there, do as others do. If they eat, you eat; if they sleep, you sleep; and above all, speak only when spoken to."

Juan had been in the house of Destiny three days before he was noticed, and then Destiny said to him, "Do you have a complaint?"

"Yes," said Juan. "I want the same *suerte* as that possessed by my brother Pedro."

"Predestination rules against that," said El Destino. "Yet, since you have gone to so much trouble to get here, I will help you. Return to your brother's home and ask him for his sister-in-law in marriage. Thanks to Pedro, she now has a *granja* in her own name. But there is one condition: after the wedding you must never refer to the property as belonging to you. You must always say, '*Es de mi mujer* [it belongs to my wife].'" With that, Juan was dismissed.

He married the sister of his brother's wife.

One day while out looking over the *granja* he met a stranger. "Whose land is this?" asked the man.

"It belongs to my wife," said Juan.

Days later some men were admiring this property. "It is an ideal farm," they said.

Then turning to Juan, who stood near, they asked, "To whom does this beautiful farm belong?"

"It is mine," said Juan.

These men went on their way. Suddenly, Juan realized that the field of ripe wheat was ablaze. He was quick to gather the reason for this and ran after the strangers. "Listen!" he called. "Listen! I lied. This field belongs to my wife."

The fire lifted and was out immediately.

Never, after that, did Juan forget. His Destiny was that he was to live all the rest of his life tied to the apron strings of his wife.

Chapter Eight

⤸ SILBADO

THIS WAS A YOUTH WHO WAS SO restless and disobedient that his mother found it necessary to turn him over to an *ayo* (a tutor) for his training and education. The new order in his life had hardly begun when he ran away.

He followed a road out of town and then entered the mountains. After two weeks of wandering with no recommendation whatever either to God or the devil, he came to the shore of a large body of water. He made a raft and set sail for nowhere in particular. Ten days and nights had passed before he reached land. This country was covered with a growth resembling bamboo. Some of it reached fourteen meters high. He found a trail and was following it, all the while wondering where it led, when he heard the trot-trot of a horse. He dropped to the ground and hid.

A giant on a giant-sized horse came along the trail. He stopped near where Silbado was hidden. The latter heard him mumble something about a good wheat harvest, and then it dawned on him that he was not in a canebrake but in a wheat field.

The horse became restless and the giant looked to the ground, doubtless thinking of a snake. He saw Silbado, leaned from his saddle, and picked him up.

142

"What a curious little plaything," said the giant, "I shall take this *monito* to my daughter."

This girl was fourteen years old and fourteen meters tall. She was thrilled with her new toy, and presently she and her father began making a cage in which to keep Silbado. It was large and more like a house than a cage. Before supper the giantess took him to a bathtub to wash him, and he almost drowned. The tub was several meters long, and the water was over his head. At supper he was given a bowl of broth. He had to stand on tiptoes to reach into the bowl. The girl took him to a piano and placed him on the keys. She was amused by the noise he made running and skipping along, back and forth, from one end of the instrument to the other.

The governor of a city nearby sent a request that the strange little *monito* be brought to him so the people could see for themselves the unusual creature that had been found in a wheat field. The girl picked up the cage, placed it on her shoulder, and, accompanied by her father, went to the city.

The people were so amazed they decided to celebrate for three days. These giants stuffed their lunch baskets and went to a nearby forest, where they prepared camp. Silbado's mistress hung his cage from a limb of a large tree; and the music, eating, and dancing began.

During the celebration a large eagle swooped down, clutched the cage in his claws, and flew away. Finally the cage, or house, was dropped in the sea. Luckily, Silbado floated toward another shore some days away, where his house was thrown on land by a tidal wave and Silbado escaped.

"This is what disobedience has brought me," said he. "If ever I get home, I shall listen more to my mother."

After much wandering, *a la buena de Dios*, he finally arrived home.

The friends of his *camada* (age) asked Silbado many questions and were carried away by the narrative of his amazing adventures.

"We want to see all this for ourselves," they said.

It was very evident that they did not believe what they had been told, and Silbado felt so compromised he agreed to take them to the territory of the giants; however, his mother said he needed school more than new adventures.

Ten years drifted by, and there was never a day that someone did not remind him of the wild story he had told about seeing giants. They began calling him Catorce.

"Listen, Catorce," they would say. "Tell us that tale again. Now let's see; that *chamaca* was fourteen years old and she was fourteen meters tall, and the wheat was fourteen meters high, and surely the height of the horse was fourteen meters. Ay, Catorce!"

Finally, since his mother had passed away and he was not needed around the place, he told his ten friends that he was tired of being called a liar.

We shall leave within a week on that adventure you have asked for, if it so please you, and if you have the *agallas* [guts]," he said.

After two weeks of travel over the mountains they came to the sea, where they built a large raft and shoved off, hoping for all sorts of thrills.

Once ashore again, they followed the beach. At last they saw a large house. Upon approaching it they found it closed. However, the corral was open and they entered, sat down in the corner, and rested.

Suddenly, there were noises like claps of thunder. They were caused by a giant who slammed doors when he came into the corral from the house. He saw them. He immediately shut the gate to the corral and built a large fire. One of Silbado's friends was picked up, put on a spit, and roasted alive. Then the giant, after eating the man, returned to the house but forgot to close the door.

"We are in a bad fix, Silbado," said one of the men. "We must find a way out of here. Sh . . . come; let's follow him."

They found the giant asleep on a mat. Returning to the corral, they heated an iron bar until it glowed; then they went to the monster and stabbed him through the heart. When they were sure he was dead, they fled to their raft on the beach.

They reached the raft just in time, since another giant was hot on their heels. This big fellow took two steps into the sea after them, struck the raft a side blow with his hand, and three of the men were drowned.

Out at sea again, the raft ran into a storm, and all aboard were lost except Silbado.

Reaching land, he began wandering and came to a city where

all the vaqueros rode bareback. He asked why they didn't use saddles.

"*Pues, no es la costumbre*," was the answer he received to his question.

He made a saddle and persuaded a man to try it out. The vaquero liked it. He made more saddles and sold them. And after that he made bridles.

He had become rich as a saddlemaker and decided to get married.

"That is all very good," said a friend, "but there are some things you need to know. Here in our country a *matrimonio* [a married couple] is buried together should one of them die. Are you willing to be buried alive should your wife die?"

"Yes," said Silbado.

He had been married two years when his wife died. He was placed in a box and was carried into a large cave with the body of his wife. After some hours he took out his knife and cut a hole in his box.

He escaped, and after much groping he found an opening to the cave. In the dark of the night that followed, Silbado reached the sea, where he found a small boat.

Many days passed on the water and in the mountains before he reached home again.

"*Gracias a Dios*," he said. "Never, if it be God's will, shall I leave this place again."

↰ SATAN AND THE BOY

ONCE UPON A TIME THERE WAS A BOY who, while seeking work, met Satan himself.

It was on the outskirts of a town that this boy encountered a well-dressed man and, after greetings, told the stranger that he was seeking employment.

"I have been looking for a *mozo*," said the señor. "Do you know how to read?"

"Sí, Señor," answered the youth.

"That is too bad; I want a boy who cannot read," said the man.

Then the boy said: "In that case, possibly, you will give work to my brother. He is *muy listo*, but hasn't learned to read yet. On up the way you will likely meet him."

The youth proceeded along in the direction he had taken, and when out of sight of the man, he doubled back, cut across a chaparral, stopped, put his poncho and hat on backward, and by running fast, came into the road ahead of the stranger. And presently they met.

The señor, or Satan, for indeed it was he, greeted him, presuming this youth to be the brother of the one he had just met, and asked where he was going.

"I am out looking for work," said the boy.

"Can you read?" asked Satan.

"No, señor," answered the youth.

"I have been looking for a *mozo* to keep my office and library clean," said Satan.

After taking over his new job the boy, by stealing glances at the titles of the books on the library shelves, realized for the first time who his master was, and whenever the latter was away from home, he read with deep interest one book after another, and became a master in diabolical arts.

However, one day Satan discovered him reading and was furious. He was preparing to flog him when the boy, using his newly acquired skills, changed into a jackrabbit. Immediately, in order to catch him, Satan became a greyhound, and was about to pounce upon him when his intended victim changed into a dove. Not to be outdone by a mere youth, Satan metamorphosed into a hawk. The race was swift and desperate with much darting about on the part of both of them. The hawk, by maneuvering skillfully, was gaining on the dove, when the latter changed into a pebble and fell to the earth. Thereupon, the hawk became a grain of rice. The pebble immediately changed into a rooster, who found the rice and ate it. Since then, Satan has always kept a weather eye out for tricks when in the presence of boys.

⤷ SOLOMON THE WISE

IT IS SAID THAT SOLOMON WASN'T always discreet in the way he illustrated a truth.

Once he was walking along a street, pondering the weakness of human nature. One of many in a crowd that followed him asked, "Are women good or bad?"

"There are as many kinds of women as there are women in this world," said Solomon; "but in general they are selfish, untruthful, and bad."

"In that case would it be right to point out any one of them as an example?"

"Yes," said Solomon, "we will begin with my mother." He called his mother, who was following at a distance. "*Mamá*," he said, "there is a question that bothers us. We would like to know whether you are bad or good."

"Son, I am good. Do you doubt it?"

Solomon turned to the crowd and asked if anyone felt any wiser, now that his mother had made her comment.

Later that day the shrewd king called one of his servants and said, "Have no fear of consequences. Tomorrow I want you to walk with my mother into the mountains. She won't care to listen to all you have to say; but regardless of her anger, you are to tell her that she is beautiful, young, and lovely. Shower her with *piropos* [flattery]. Remember, half a word won't be enough. In short, make love to her, and tell me later what she said to you."

That afternoon the mother came to Solomon and said, "My son, I have brought you this servant. He has been provoking me. He has insulted you, his king, by saying things to me that I prefer not to mention."

"What would you have me do with him?" asked Solomon. "Let's let him go. I will take care of him later."

"Don't ask me again to associate with anyone so uncouth. This I ask as a favor," said the mother.

"But I want you to go out again, with another servant. I command it."

This time she was accompanied into the fields. They came to a stream and sat on the bank. Later, when she found her son, she said to him, "Son, you are a *cornudo* [pander]. Is there no limit to you? That servant should be hanged, for he wanted to put his arms about me. He was worse than the last."

"Just one more, *mamacita*, and this will be all."

"I shall go only because you have the power to command me to do so," she said.

Solomon's mother and his servant walked along a boulevard. They came to a bench and sat for awhile to rest. This man commented on the spring flowers and particularly on the lilies of the field; he quoted poetry in which there was much mention of love. He made casual reference to this and that girl who passed by, but seemingly ignored the woman by his side.

Then she took the initiative, and before it was over she had invited him to her bedroom after night had drawn over the city. "Knock on my door three times," she said, "and I shall let you in."

The servant reported all this to Solomon. The latter changed clothes with the servant and kept his appointment for him. He knocked on the mother's door and was told to come in; but he refused, saying in a muffled voice that she should open for him.

"My son!" she gasped when he entered.

Then she began to weep, and Solomon asked what she would have him do with the servants for their part in the trick that had been played on her.

"Nothing," she said. "Let them go in peace."

"Mother," said Solomon, "only a few days ago you told me you were good. This nature of forgiveness on your part proves that. On the other hand, it was not a good woman who invited a man to her bedroom at this hour of the night. We don't need God's help for our goodness, Mother, but we do need it to protect us from evil. Keep that in mind and we will understand each other."

╰┐ EL CABALLERO PORFIADO

THIS WAS A KING WHO WAS TOLD BY a dream spirit that he would lose his one and only daughter. In order to be sure that nothing should happen to the princess, he had her moved to a large and luxurious chamber beneath the castle. Here she was placed behind seven locks, and the keys were handed over to a trusted housekeeper with instructions that she was to serve the girl three meals a day, make her bed of a morning, and keep the place clean.

The princess, who was beautiful, modest, and intelligent,

seemed little concerned with the mandate of her father, the king.
She painted, practiced her music, did embroidery, and was con-
tented until one night when she was touched by an invisible hand.
The following morning she had the servant fetch the king.

"Father," she said, "last night a Christian came to my room and
placed his hands upon me."

"Don't be foolish," said the king. "It is impossible for a Christian, Moor, or anyone else to enter here. You are behind seven locks,
and these have one key each. Surely you were dreaming."

The following morning she sent for him again and said she was
positive some man had come to her bed and placed his hand upon
her brow.

"Listen, my child," said the king. "Would you have me believe
that you are losing your mind? Don't bother me again, or I shall
flog you."

The father called the maid, and they searched every nook and
corner of the underground chambers for evidence of someone's having entered the place. Nowhere was there any indication that a
stranger had been there.

The following night, as the princess lay awake, she felt a move-
ment on the covers of her bed; and presently a hand rested upon
her brow. She did not scream, but calmly asked, "Who are you?"

"Don't fear," said a voice. "It is I, the one destined to take you
from this place to Los Llanos de Apa, a long sleep from here. As
for my name, it will be your name in marriage within ten years."

Dawn had removed the stars from heaven and had covered the
eastern sky with gleams of a new day, when the maid opened the
last of the seven locks and entered the chamber of the princess.

"*Válgame Dios!*" she gasped. "She is gone! *Válgame Dios!* What
is to become of me?"

The father was called. He faced defeat with dignity and vented
no rage upon the servant. It was as though he had known all the
while that seven locks and seven keys could not prevent the con-
stant and forward strides of time and destiny.

"I should have known," he said. "I should have known. The
dream spirit spoke the words of fate."

For weeks past, a venturesome young knight had been writing
to the princess. A bribe had smoothed the way for this. Letters of

love had led to their engagement, and the young man had studied and schemed in order to find some way to free the girl, but all to no avail. So it was that when he learned of her mysterious disappearance, his dilemma was so deep he felt unequal to cope with it and took to his feet and wandered away.

A voice came to him from a cabin near his path. "Where goest thou, young man?" it asked.

"I go nowhere," he answered. "I drift *a la buena de Dios.* Be it known unto you, old man and old woman, that the girl I love has been spirited away. A strict father, seven locks, and seven keys could not hold her. There is no hope of happiness for me. Thus it is that I have placed my lot in the hands of blind fate and shall drift until I die."

"Don't be despondent," said the old woman from where she stood with her husband in the doorway of the cabin. "If you knew where to find the girl, what would you do?"

"I would go to her immediately," said the youth.

"I can tell you where to find her," said the old man. "She and the magician who freed her stopped by here in their flight to Los Llanos de Apa. Follow on toward the south and you will reach these plains; and let's hope, by good chance, that you come to a small hut with a large door of oak wood."

The young knight bought three tortillas from the old woman, and with many thanks he left and continued toward the south.

After some hours of travel he came to a tree; and while he was resting and eating in its shade, three small ants came to where he sat. He dropped crumbs for them and was surprised when one addressed him as follows: "We are grateful for the food. Here is one of my feet. If you should ever need to become an ant, hold this foot between your thumb and index finger and say, '*Dios y hormiga.*' And when you wish to be yourself again, you are to say, '*Dios y cristiano.*'"

After more wandering he came to a lagoon, where he drank and rested. A hawk that had been soaring above him came down and lit nearby. The young knight took his second tortilla from beneath his blouse and gave part of it to the bird. The latter ate, sat still for a moment, and then asked, "Good young man, why are you traveling over this wide desert?"

"I am looking for Los Llanos de Apa," he answered. "I hope to find there a girl who wandered away from home."

"I have much ill-boding for you, my young friend. You take dire chances with your life. Seeking afoot you will get nowhere; and eventually you will die of thirst. Look, I am going to present you with this feather. If by chance you should like to fly as a hawk, hold it between your thumb and forefinger and say, '*Dios y gavilán*,' and when you wish to become yourself again, say, '*Dios y cristiano*.'"

For two days he continued his journey from dawn to dusk. On the third day he met a lion.

"I am too near death to care what happens to me," thought the young man. "This lion will kill me, and that will be the end of it all, so why worry."

He walked up to the lion and placed a tortilla on its nose. The animal ate and said, "You have killed my need for food. May I ask where you are going?"

"I seek Los Llanos de Apa," answered the knight.

"Los Llanos are alive with wild beasts," said the lion. "They will kill you."

"That makes little difference," said the youth.

"But you are going to need help," said the lion. "Here, accept this claw. When things seem hopeless, hold it between your thumb and index finger and say, '*Dios y león*.' And when you wish to change back to yourself once again, say, '*Dios y cristiano*.'"

The knight continued on his way and presently he heard voices from somewhere within himself, and they were saying, "*Dios y león, Dios y gavilán, Dios y hormiga*, have faith."

Thereupon he took the feather and held it in accordance with the advice of the hawk. And like a child's kite, he was swooped into the air and went flying over the desert.

Shortly thereafter he found a small hut, and the door was of oak wood. Yet it was closed tight and locked from within. He took the small foot of the ant between his thumb and forefinger and said, "*Dios y hormiga*."

Presently he found a small crack beneath the door and crawled through, but barely had he caught his breath when he heard a loud voice that sang:

Jo, jo; carne y hueso huelo aquí,
Si no me la das, te como a ti.
(Ho, ho; flesh and bone I smell here,
If you do not give it to me, I shall eat you.)

A girl's voice was heard to ask, "Whom do you suspect? No one can enter here."

The *mal genio* picked up a wand, struck a table with it, and within a wink of the eye he and the missing princess were eating supper. After the meal the *genio* went about the place closing doors. He turned, said good night, and disappeared.

The ant changed back into a knight, and the latter touched the shoulder of the girl. She was startled. "If the magician finds you here he will kill you," she said.

"Not before I have learned the secrets of this place," said the knight. "How can such a little hut have so much room? How did you get here, and how do we leave?"

"When you entered what you thought was a small hut, you came into a large cavern. I don't know how I got here nor how we are to leave," said the girl.

"When you dine tomorrow," said the young man, "see what you can find out. Remember, I shall be near you all the while in the form of an ant."

Then they heard the slamming of doors about the place and presently:

Jo, jo; carne y hueso huelo aquí,
Si no me la das, te como a ti.

"*Dios y hormiga,*" said the knight. And he changed to an ant and crawled into the hem of the girl's skirt.

The magician was in a talkative mood, and before long the girl had learned that his soul was in an egg and the egg was in a dove that was in a room guarded by a large bear. Also she learned that if the egg was broken before the magic time had expired the magician would die immediately.

The *genio* went to his room, the ant changed into a knight again, and the knight changed to a lion and killed the bear. After becoming a young man again, the knight found the dove, got the egg, broke it on the forehead of the magician, and thus destroyed him.

The knight and the princess soon found their way out of the cavern, returned to civilization, and were married.

∽ DON CACAHUATE

ONE DAY DON CACAHUATE (PEANUT) was strolling about a plaza, when he met a señorita who wasn't hard to look at.

"*Escucha tú*, señorita," he said. "What is your name?"

Timidly, she blushed and then replied, "*Pos*, Flora Rosa Rosales."

"Come, Flora Rosa," he teased, "let's you and me start a flower garden."

It is said they were married some time thereafter.

A friend took Don Cacahuate to task for his laziness.

"Don't you ever have a desire to work?" he asked.

"*Cómo no?*" was the answer from our hero. "I have the desire, but *lo aguanto* (I can resist it)."

Often Don Cacahuate was late getting home from his carousing. Flora, his wife, began locking him out. One morning about three o'clock he tried the door; and when he found it locked, he began screaming, "Flora, open the door for me, open the door, I've been cut."

Flora came running from the house in her nightgown. "Where, where have you been cut?"

"Out, stupid, out from a bunch of horny roughnecks. Come, it is late; let's go to bed."

Civic authorities never permitted Don Cacahuate to settle at any place for long. Like Till Eulenspiegel, he generally left a town just a hop and a half ahead of an officer of the law, or a mob that had been the butt of his pranks. However, upon one occasion, the *presidente municipal* generously gave him one hour in which to leave the region. Don Cacahuate rushed home and shouted, "*Oye vieja*, we are leaving on the railroad. Get your things together in a hurry; we have to be at the station within thirty minutes."

Going places by train was Flora's weakness. She ran about the place in a happy flurry, gathering her few little possessions in a *morral*, and hurried after her husband, who reached the station well ahead of her and kept on walking with long strides down the track.

"*Epa* [listen], Cacahuate," she called, "people catch the train at the station."

"What train, by my father," said Don Cacahuate as he kept right on hotfooting it down the track. "I didn't tell you we were going by train, but on the *ferrocarril* [railroad]; hurry, walk faster, or the syndicate will be charging us for the use of their tracks."

Once he tried his luck in Texas. He learned to wear a Stetson and Levi's. Also, he learned a smattering of English. When he returned to Chihuahua, he began showing off his new language.

One day, as he followed a wagon road, riding his famous horse Pinto Verde, he met a man driving six burros hitched to a heavy wagon. Our Don, trying hard to look and act the part of a *tejano*, rolled himself a cigarette and approached the wagon. Holding his unlit *pita* before him, he said, "Aló, *compadre*; you gottie maeches [matches, understood as *machos*, mules]?"

"*No, señor*," responded the driver. "*Son puros burros* [just burros]."

Don Cacahuate and Pinto Verde were following a narrow trail in the mountains one day, when they found it blocked by a dead animal. Don Cacahuate couldn't make out what it was, so he dismounted for a close inspection.

"*Válgame Dios!*" he exclaimed. "I wonder what killed this mosquito!"

Flora Rosa Rosales de Cacahuate was very coquettish. She flirted around so much that Don Cacahuate, eventually, began to doubt the paternity of his three sons. One morning he invited the boys to ride with him into the mountains. At a place overlooking a canyon, he stopped and said, "Do you see that doe over there across the canyon?"

"Where?" asked the oldest boy. "I see no doe."

"Where?" asked the second son. "I see no doe."

"*Ay, caráy!*" said the third and youngest boy. "There are a doe and a fawn."

"How do you see a doe and a fawn when the rest of us don't even see a doe?"

"I didn't say I saw them," said the little boy, "but I hear the fawn sucking its mother."

"That's my boy!" exclaimed the father. "You, at least, are my son."

Once while herding cattle in a rainstorm our great man and hero crossed his leg over the pommel of his saddle and rolled himself a cigarette. Then he felt for matches. He found none and began cursing his luck. Pinto Verde heard him and appreciated the embarrassment of his master. The horse watched the thundercloud; and at the proper time and split second, he sprang skyward into a thunderhead. Don Cacahuate lit his *pita* on a flash of lightning.

Once Don Cacahuate went on his horse to Zacatecas to attend a convention. When he reached the city, Pinto Verde became aware of the glad-happy rhythm made by his hooves on the cobbled streets; and he put on such a show of fancy singlefooting a la equestrian terpsichore that his feet sounded a merry tune—*Za-ca-TE-cas, Za-ca-TE-cas, Za-ca-TE-cas*. But he overdid it and broke smack dab in two. And then there was no other sound from his shoes except *Za-ca, Za-ca, Za-ca, Za-ca.*

"Woah," said Don Cacahuate, "there is something missing. *Dónde estarán las te-cas* [where could the *tecas* be]?"

He stopped, looked back, and saw the rear of Pinto Verde a half-block away. But that didn't bother him. He simply waited until the *te-cas* caught up with the *Za-ca*, and continued on down the street with more caution, saying, *ZA-ca-TE-cas, ZA-ca-TE-cas, ZA-ca-TE-cas.*"

Another time Don Cacahuate put a few peaches in a *morral,*

picked up his old muzzle-loader, and went deer hunting. While working his way through a meadow where the grass was waist high, he saw a large buck. After much nervous fumbling he succeeded in getting powder and *taco* down the muzzle of his gun. Then he quickly reached into his shot pouch—but found nothing. He had just finished eating a peach, so he rammed the seed into his gun, took a jittery aim, and fired. The deer fell. Don Cacahuate ran to the buck, but before he reached him the animal had gotten to his feet and had run away.

Three years later Don Cacahuate was in the same meadow hunting, and this time the grass was up to his shoulders. He found no deer but did find a peach tree laden with ripe fruit. He climbed into the branches and was picking and eating peaches, when, by chance, he looked down. Imagine his amazement when he realized his tree was running across the meadow, with him high on a limb. This was the same animal he had shot in the head with a peach seed three years before. Gently he climbed down, killed the deer with his *daga*, took it home, and had venison and peach preserves for supper.

Do you doubt this? Well, we can take care of that. He planted one of the seeds in his patio, and the tree came up and stands as evidence of the truth of this tale and the unquestionable honesty of Don Cacahuate.

DEATH COMES AT A TROT

"GIL PEREZ AT YOUR SERVICE," SAID the little man with a straight back and bowlegs. "Ah, so my friend Miguel Contreras of Patos sends you to me. Come in, *señor*. Seat yourself. You speak Spanish like a Mexican. West Texas? *Qué casualidad*; I have broken horses there."

"In addition to making your acquaintance, horses are the reason for my visit," I said.

There were some minutes given to a rodeo of conventionalities during which time I shifted the weight of conversation to him.

"Like you, *señor*, I love horses. I never forget them, and when they die it gives me a desire to weep. *Sí, señor*, most of my friends, horses and men alike, are now gone, and there is little I can do to console myself except at times to recall the good old days. And did you ever notice, *señor*, how hard it is to be happy in the memory of the dead when they were better to you than you to them? I recall—"

"At last," thought I. "Here comes the *cuento*."

"I recall," he continued, "a little horse I used to ride while working at the Piedra Blanca. His name was Chepito. No man or woman has ever understood me as did he. Though man and horse, we worked together like brothers, were happy and sad, hungry and tired together. One day, however, it was Gil Perez and not Chepito who did not remember to do the right thing in the right way, and the poor little brown horse—well, he lost his life. You see, *señor*, I staked him one night in a grove of palmillas, and he, tangling himself in the rope, broke a leg.

"Another was a large bay. We called him El Diablo. How this horse liked to pitch! But don't imagine for that it was make-believe. He meant every stiff-legged blast of it. He and I had a great time, for when once I learned to stick with him I would mount, run my thumbs along his neck to his ears, and scream like a panther; and then I would begin a job of clawing leather you should have seen. The very memory of him makes my bones ache from the base of my skull to my ankles.

"But it was Gil Perez again who was thoughtless, and while showing off before the *señoritas* in Músquiz on a Sunday afternoon, I ran El Diablo over a log, and his neck was broken.

"Once while taking a herd of cattle from Santo Domingo to the border at Del Rio, we had camped near an old placer mine. The next morning the remuda was herded into an angle formed by two deep pits and a slag heap. Most of the men had gotten their mounts and were gone when the cook called me. You see, I had been on guard that night.

"'What horse do you want, Gil?' he asked. 'While you eat, I'll saddle him for you.'

"'Oh,' I said 'choose him yourself. Anything will do.'

"After breakfast I went to the improvised corral, and behold there stood a horse I had never seen before. He was a *grullo*, with black hooves, black mane and tail, and a fringe of black on each ear. When he saw me, he lowered his head, pointed his ears toward me, and breathed an uneasy warning. I reached for the reins. He snorted, sprang into the air, and barely missed me with his left hoof. *Qué sorpresa!* He had none of the marks of a *ladino*. His nose was straight, ears large, neck short and slender, and his eyes were as mild as those of a doe.

"But he wheeled and kicked, broke the reins, and headed for the shafts. He slipped on the loose slag and fell. His right hip was broken and we killed him. Whenever I recall the *grullo*, I feel death cheated me out of a good horse."

There was a pause.

"You surely know some *cuentos* and *historias*," I said, "like for instance the devil changing into a horse, or Pinto Verde, the famous mount of Don Cacahuate, or the favorite horse of Benito Canales, Pancho Villa, or the Marquez de Aguayo."

"No, *señor*, I recall no particular story," he replied.

"Once in Piedras Negras," I prompted further, "a stanza from the poems of the Negrito Poeta was quoted to me. The officer reminded me in this stanza that death like a *caballo* might come at a trot. Did you ever hear of Godmother Death riding a horse?"

"*A sí cómo no?*" he said. "My friend Daniel Cantú and other *vaqueros* from a *costeña* ranch on the Gulf of Mexico in Tamaulipas were camped one night on an island. His private mount was a large broken-eared gray called Gacho. Since this horse refused to run with a remuda, they belled him before he was driven with the bunch into the mesquite south of camp for the night.

"After the *muchachos* had had their *frijoles*, *tortillas*, meat, and *café*, they leaned against their bedding, smoked, and listened to the roaring of the surf about a kilometer to the east. Presently stories were told, a song or two was sung, and all lay down for the night. Daniel couldn't sleep. He was afraid the gray Gacho would slip by the camp and try to swim the bay to mainland.

"He had lain for some time in a half-daze listening to the bell and the surf and watching a black cloud coming in from the Gulf when he became aware of the fact that Gacho had quit the remuda and was on his way to the pass. He arose from his bed, crept to a bush by the trail, and waited in order to turn him back.

"But there was something strange about the bell. No horse without a rider or driver ever gave it such an even and purposeful rhythm.

" '*Pues qué tendrá?*' thought Daniel. 'Could someone be riding him?'

"But behold twelve fighting men in silver armor and riding white horses came into view. A full moon was shining from directly above. The storm cloud out over the Gulf was cut at quick intervals by lightning, and the thunder was lost in the roar of the surf.

"On they came at a slow, even trot. Daniel, his heart in his throat, dropped to the ground behind the bush and watched. Now they were even with the camp. They passed in pairs and were followed by a priest in black, riding a black mule.

" 'How strange,' thought Daniel. 'They are from a thousand years ago, from a land of yesteryear. But, look! What is this?'

"Two skeletons carrying a corpse on a litter followed the knights, and next came a woman dressed in white. It was La Madrina Muerte—yes, the Godmother. The fact that she rode Gacho seemed to have little meaning for Daniel until—until he awoke— awoke and sat up in bed.

"It was a dream. Yet, was it a dream? The bell had been south with the remuda; now it was north and it tinkled a slow, even saddle trot. He listened until the sound of it mingled sadly with the surf, then went to sleep again."

"Did he find his horse next morning?" I asked.

"No, *señor*; Daniel says there is no doubt that the Madrina took him away."